INTRODUCTORY NUMERICAL ANALYSIS

Introductory Numerical Analysis

ANTHONY J. PETTOFREZZO

The Florida State University

D. C. HEATH AND COMPANY

BOSTON ENGLEWOOD INDIANAPOLIS SAN FRANCISCO
ATLANTA DALLAS

COVER PHOTO by Reynolds, Stone from *The Connoisseur*

LIBRARY OF CONGRESS CATALOG CARD NUMBER: 66-21730

PRINTED SEPTEMBER 1966

TO MY PARENTS

ROSE AND JOSEPH

PREFACE

The subject of NUMERICAL ANALYSIS has assumed an increasingly important role in the undergraduate curriculum of our colleges and universities during the past decade. A number of texts on numerical analysis are available. However, most of these are written with two groups of people in mind: one group consists of graduate students to whom a large-scale digital computer is available; the other group consists of applied mathematicians, engineers, and scientists working in the digital computer field. I have written this book primarily for the undergraduate mathematics major, engineering student, or future high school mathematics teacher who needs some understanding of the underlying principles involved in numerical analysis. This is not primarily a text on methods, although some attention is paid to algorithms. In general, comparisons of the relative merits of several methods of solution of a problem are made in terms of the principles and assumptions involved, rather than in terms of computer time, storage, etc. Such a text as this is especially well-suited for undergraduate and graduate students at colleges and universities where large-scale digital computing facilities may not be available.

Since the field of NUMERICAL ANALYSIS represents a broad area of mathematics, a selection of topics must be made. Only those topics considered appropriate to a first course are treated. Many of the topics for this book are basic to the study of numerical analysis in terms of the classical approach. Others were selected because of personal interest.

The main theme of the book is interpolation from the standpoint of finite differences, least squares theory, and harmonic analysis. Some attention is paid to the methods of solution of simultaneous equations which are immediately applicable to least squares problems. The topic of summation of series is treated. Especially important to future teachers of mathematics is the chapter dealing with the relationships between the calculus of finite differences and the calculus of infinitesimals. Chapters on the numerical solutions of ordinary differential equations and approximations through Fourier series are included.

More than 70 worked-out illustrative examples have been included as an aid to the reader in his mastery of the concepts and methods presented. In some instances, the solution to the same problem has been worked several times by different methods to illustrate the variety of approaches open to the computer and to compare the relative merits of the different methods. There are over 280 exercises, many of which have several parts, that range from drill problems to those requiring some degree of ingenuity on the part of the student. Answers are provided to those problems having numerical solutions.

The only prerequisite required of the reader is an understanding of the material presented in a standard differential and integral calculus course. Such a course should have included material on infinite series, functions of several variables, and ordinary differential equations. Some familiarity with determinants is assumed. An appendix containing definitions and several theorems from elementary determinant theory is included for those students lacking any knowledge of determinants.

There are a number of people to whom I am directly or indirectly indebted for the completion of this book. I am particularly indebted to the many mathematicians of the Electro-Mechanical Laboratory at the White Sands Missile Range, N.M., who, many years ago, kindled my interest in numerical analysis. Thanks are due a number of reviewers, including Professor Michael Lione of Newark College of Engineering, for their suggestions and criticisms. I also wish to thank those students at Montclair State College who labored with the preliminary versions of the book. A sincere note of appreciation is due my wife, Betty, for typing the manuscripts and for her encouragement. Finally, I wish to thank the staff of D. C. Heath and Company for their cooperation during the production of this book.

ANTHONY J. PETTOFREZZO

CONTENTS

INTRODUCTORY NUMERICAL ANALYSIS

1

Finite Differences

I. INTRODUCTION

A functional relationship between two variables may be expressed in several ways. Among the more common ways is a mathematical formula, a verbal rule, or a set of points (values). Empirical data are usually given in the form of a set of points which may or may not be equally spaced with regard to the independent variable. In elementary mathematics, *interpolation* is defined as the process of determining intermediate values of a function from a set of points. The Danish mathematician Thiele described this as *the art of reading between the lines of a table*. In dealing with functions whose analytical representation may or may not be known, we may, with the knowledge of certain values of the independent and dependent variables, substitute or define another analytic function which approximates the original function. This is interpolation in its broadest sense.

The basis of the subject of interpolation lies in two important theorems proved by Weierstrass in 1885 which may be stated as follows:

1. Every function $f(x)$ which is continuous on a closed interval (a, b) can be approximated to any desired degree of accuracy by a polynomial $p(x)$; that is, there exists a $p(x)$ such that

$$|f(x) - p(x)| < \epsilon$$

for $a \leq x \leq b$, where ϵ is any preassigned positive value.

2. Every continuous function $f(x)$ of period 2π can be approximated to any desired degree of accuracy by a trigonometric series $T(x)$ of the form

$$T(x) = a_0 + a_1 \sin x + a_2 \sin 2x + \cdots + a_n \sin nx$$
$$+ b_1 \cos x + b_2 \cos 2x + \cdots + b_n \cos nx;$$

that is, it is possible to determine a $T(x)$ such that

$$|f(x) - T(x)| < \epsilon$$

for $a \leq x \leq b$, where ϵ is any preassigned positive value.

A basic problem in numerical analysis is to determine, with some criteria in mind, a simple formula representing a functional relationship exhibited by a set of empirical data. For a given set of $n + 1$ points (x_0, y_0), (x_1, y_1), ..., (x_n, y_n), one criterion under which we may fit a curve to the data is to require that an approximation function $I(x)$ be determined such that

$$I(x_i) = y_i \quad \text{for} \quad i = 0, 1, \ldots, n.$$

This is most often the process of interpolation by the methods of finite differences and shall be one of our chief concerns in Chapter 2. The methods used in the calculus of finite differences almost always assume the form of $I(x)$ to be a rational integral function, or polynomial; that is,

$$I(x) = a + bx + cx^2 + \cdots + kx^n.$$

The calculus of finite differences is a study of the changes in functional values due to finite changes in the independent variable(s).

In this chapter, we shall examine some of the basic definitions, theorems, and relationships for the calculus of finite differences.

2. TABLES OF DIFFERENCES

Given the set of points (x_0, y_0), (x_1, y_1), ..., (x_n, y_n), determined by the relationship $y = f(x)$ such that $x_1 - x_0 = x_2 - x_1 = \cdots = x_n - x_{n-1} = h$, some constant, we shall define the quantities $y_1 - y_0, y_2 - y_1, \ldots, y_n - y_{n-1}$ as the *first differences* of the function. Symbolically, we shall denote the first differences of y by Δy_i, where the subscript i shall be the same as the second member of the difference; that is,

$$\Delta y_0 = y_1 - y_0,$$
$$\Delta y_1 = y_2 - y_1,$$
$$\cdots$$

1.1

$$\Delta y_{n-1} = y_n - y_{n-1}.$$

Differences of the first differences are called *second differences* and are denoted by $\Delta^2 y_i$; that is,

$$\Delta^2 y_0 = \Delta y_1 - \Delta y_0,$$
$$\Delta^2 y_1 = \Delta y_2 - \Delta y_1,$$
$$\cdots$$

1.2

$$\Delta^2 y_{n-2} = \Delta y_{n-1} - \Delta y_{n-2}.$$

In a similar manner, we may define the higher-order differences. In general, the *nth-order differences* of a function are defined by the formula

$$\Delta^n y_i = \Delta^{n-1} y_{i+1} - \Delta^{n-1} y_i.$$

1.3

It is possible to express differences of any order in terms of the given values of the function, $y_0, y_1, \ldots, y_n$, by successive substitutions. For example, since

$$\Delta^2 y_0 = \Delta y_1 - \Delta y_0$$

and

$$\Delta y_i = y_{i+1} - y_i,$$

we have

$$\Delta^2 y_0 = (y_2 - y_1) - (y_1 - y_0)$$
$$= y_2 - 2y_1 + y_0.$$

In a similar manner,

$$\Delta^3 y_0 = \Delta^2 y_1 - \Delta^2 y_0$$
$$= (\Delta y_2 - \Delta y_1) - (\Delta y_1 - \Delta y_0)$$
$$= [(y_3 - y_2) - (y_2 - y_1)] - [(y_2 - y_1) - (y_1 - y_0)]$$
$$= y_3 - 3y_2 + 3y_1 - y_0.$$

In general,

$$\Delta^n y_0 = y_n - \binom{n}{1} y_{n-1} + \binom{n}{2} y_{n-2} + \cdots + (-1)^n y_0$$

$$= \sum_{i=0}^{n} (-1)^i \binom{n}{i} y_{n-i},$$

1.4

where $\binom{n}{i}$ is the binomial coefficient defined by

$$\binom{n}{i} = \frac{n!}{i! \, (n-i)!}.$$

1.5

Schematically, we may represent the successive differences of a set of values of a function by means of a *diagonal difference table* as shown in Table 1.1.

TABLE 1.1

DIAGONAL DIFFERENCE TABLE

x	y	Δy	$\Delta^2 y$	$\Delta^3 y$	$\Delta^4 y$	$\cdots$	$\Delta^n y$
x_0	y_0						
		Δy_0					
x_1	y_1		$\Delta^2 y_0$				
		Δy_1		$\Delta^3 y_0$			
x_2	y_2		$\Delta^2 y_1$		$\Delta^4 y_0$		
		Δy_2		$\Delta^3 y_1$			
x_3	y_3		$\Delta^2 y_2$		$\Delta^4 y_1$		$\Delta^n y_0$
		Δy_3		$\Delta^3 y_2$			
x_4	y_4		$\Delta^2 y_3$				
		Δy_4					
x_5	y_5				$\Delta^4 y_{n-4}$		
				$\Delta^3 y_{n-3}$			
			$\Delta^2 y_{n-2}$				
		Δy_{n-1}					
x_n	y_n						

Each entry in the body of a diagonal difference table is the difference of the adjacent entries above and below in the column to the left. The entry y_0 is called the *leading term*, and the first terms in each column, $\Delta y_0, \Delta^2 y_0, \ldots, \Delta^n y_0$, are called the *leading differences*. Note that a difference table for $n + 1$ points has n first differences, $n - 1$ second differences, $n - 2$ third differences, etc.

Table 1.2 represents a diagonal difference table in terms of the given values of the function.

TABLE 1.2

x	y	Δy	$\Delta^2 y$	$\Delta^3 y$	$\cdots$	$\Delta^n y$
x_0	y_0					
		$y_1 - y_0$				
x_1	y_1		$y_2 - 2y_1 + y_0$			
		$y_2 - y_1$		$y_3 - 3y_2 + 3y_1 - y_0$		
x_2	y_2		$y_3 - 2y_2 + y_1$			$\cdots$
		$y_3 - y_2$		$\cdot$		$\sum_{i=0}^{n}(-1)^i\binom{n}{i}y_{n-i}$
x_3	y_3		$\cdot$	$\cdot$		
$\cdot$	$\cdot$	$\cdot$	$\cdot$			
$\cdot$	$\cdot$	$\cdot$		$y_n - 3y_{n-1} + 3y_{n-2} - y_{n-3}$		
$\cdot$	$\cdot$		$y_n - 2y_{n-1} + y_{n-2}$			
		$y_n - y_{n-1}$				
x_n	y_n					

EXAMPLE 1.   Construct a difference table for the set of points $(-3, -25)$, $(-1, 1)$, $(1, 3)$, $(3, 29)$, and $(5, 205)$.

Solution: Labeling the points $(x_0, y_0), (x_1, y_1), \ldots, (x_4, y_4)$, respectively, we construct Difference Table A from Table 1.1 and the definition of differences.

Difference Table A

x	y	Δy	$\Delta^2 y$	$\Delta^3 y$	$\Delta^4 y$
-3	-25				
		26			
-1	1		-24		
		2		48	
1	3		24		78
		26		126	
3	29		150		
		176			
5	205				

EXAMPLE 2. Express $\Delta^4 y_0$ in terms of the successive entries of the table in Example 1 and evaluate.

Solution: From equation (1.4),

$$\Delta^4 y_0 = y_4 - \binom{4}{1} y_3 + \binom{4}{2} y_2 - \binom{4}{3} y_1 + \binom{4}{4} y_0$$

$$= y_4 - 4y_3 + 6y_2 - 4y_1 + y_0.$$

Therefore,

$$\Delta^4 y_0 = 205 - 4(29) + 6(3) - 4(1) + (-25)$$

$$= 78.$$

This agrees with the results of the difference table in Example 1.

EXERCISES

1. Construct difference tables for the following sets of points:
   (a) $(2, 0), (3, 1), (4, 8), (5, 21)$;
   (b) $(0, -5), (1, -3), (2, 1), (3, 8), (4, 14)$;
   (c) $(-3, 2), (-1, 12), (1, 21), (3, 33)$;
   (d) $(2.0, -9), (2.5, 0), (3.0, 3), (3.5, 12), (4.0, 39), (4.5, 96)$;
   (e) $(0, 3), (3, 9), (6, 15), (9, 21)$.

2. Construct a difference table for the function $y = x^3 - 2x^2 + 7$ with $x_0 = 0$ and $h = 0.5$. Consider ten successive points.

3. Show that:

   (a) $\binom{n}{r} = \binom{n}{n-r}$;

   (b) $\binom{n+1}{r} = \binom{n}{r} + \binom{n}{r-1}$;

   (c) $\binom{n+1}{r+1} = \frac{n+1}{r+1}\binom{n}{r}$;

   (d) $\sum_{r=0}^{n} \binom{n}{r} = 2^n$;

   (e) $\sum_{r=0}^{n} (-1)^r \binom{n}{r} = 0$;

   (f) $\sum_{r=0}^{n} \binom{n}{r}^2 = \binom{2n}{n}$.

4. Find $\Delta^5 y_0$ in terms of successive functional values.

5. Express $\Delta^n y_k$ in terms of successive functional values.

6. Find the next term of the following sequences by extending their difference tables:
   (a) 1, 4, 10, 20, 35, 56;
   (b) $-1, 0, 1, 8, 27, 64$;
   (c) 2, 2, 14, 74, 242;
   (d) 1, 3, 8, 17, 32, 57, 100, 177, 320;
   (e) 14, 23, 34, 42, 59.
   What assumption has been made in each case?

7. Given the points $(2, 1), (3, 6), (4, 13), (5, 22)$, and $(6, 33)$, find y for $x = 0$. State the assumption under which the value is determined.

8. Derive equation (1.4) by means of mathematical induction.

3. SYMBOLIC OPERATORS

In order to obtain $\Delta f(x)$ for any function $f(x)$, we have to change $f(x)$ to $f(x + h)$ and then determine the difference $f(x + h) - f(x)$. The symbol Δ is called the *difference operator* since it defines this operation of obtaining the difference of two values of a function when applied to that function. The function $f(x + h)$ may be symbolically denoted by $Ef(x)$ so that

$$\Delta f(x) = Ef(x) - f(x) \qquad \textbf{1.6}$$

defines the operation of taking the first differences of $f(x)$. The symbol E is called the *shift operator* since it defines the operation of obtaining the value of a function after a shift in the independent variable by some constant h. If we omit the $f(x)$ expressions in equation (1.6), we may write the relationship between the two operators Δ and E as

$$\Delta = E - 1, \qquad \textbf{1.7}$$

or

$$E = 1 + \Delta. \qquad \textbf{1.8}$$

Careful note should be made that $f(x)$ has not been factored out. Equations (1.7) and (1.8) merely define an operational relationship.

By repeated applications of the shift operator E to $f(x)$, we have

$$E^2 f(x) = E[Ef(x)] = Ef(x + h) = f(x + 2h);$$
$$E^3 f(x) = E[E^2 f(x)] = Ef(x + 2h) = f(x + 3h).$$

In general,

$$E^n f(x) = f(x + nh), \qquad \textbf{1.9}$$

where n is a positive integer. The student should note that the operators Δ^n and E^n have been defined only for positive integral values of n. No interpretation of these operators has been made for fractional or negative values of n.

Making use of equations (1.8) and (1.9), we may write

$$f(x + nh) = E^n f(x) = (1 + \Delta)^n f(x).$$

Hence, by means of the binomial expansion of $(1 + \Delta)^n$, we have

$$f(x + nh) = f(x) + \binom{n}{1}\Delta f(x) + \binom{n}{2}\Delta^2 f(x) + \cdots + \Delta^n f(x). \qquad \textbf{1.10}$$

In terms of a given set of points $(x_0, y_0), (x_1, y_1), \ldots, (x_n, y_n)$, where $x_{i+1} - x_i = h$, equation (1.6) is interpreted as

$$\Delta y_i = E y_i - y_i, \qquad \textbf{1.11}$$

where

$$E y_i = y_{i+1}. \qquad \textbf{1.12}$$

Equation (1.9) is interpreted as

$$E^n y_i = y_{i+n}. \qquad \textbf{1.13}$$

Equation (1.10) gives us an expression for every tabular value of a function in terms of the leading term and leading differences. That is, letting $x = x_0$ and $n = i$ in equation (1.10), we have

$$y_i = y_0 + \binom{i}{1}\Delta y_0 + \binom{i}{2}\Delta^2 y_0 + \cdots + \Delta^i y_0. \qquad \textbf{1.14}$$

EXAMPLE 1.   Find $Ef(x)$ where $f(x) = 2x^3 - x$.

Solution: By definition,
$$Ef(x) = f(x + h).$$
Therefore,
$$
\begin{aligned}
E(2x^3 - x) &= 2(x + h)^3 - (x + h) \\
&= 2(x^3 + 3hx^2 + 3h^2x + h^3) - (x + h) \\
&= 2x^3 + 6hx^2 + (6h^2 - 1)x + (2h^3 - h).
\end{aligned}
$$

EXAMPLE 2.   Find $\Delta f(x)$ where $f(x) = x^2 + 3x - 1$.

Solution: By definition,
$$\Delta f(x) = f(x + h) - f(x).$$
Therefore,
$$
\begin{aligned}
\Delta(x^2 + 3x - 1) &= (x + h)^2 + 3(x + h) - 1 - (x^2 + 3x - 1) \\
&= (x^2 + 2hx + h^2 + 3x + 3h - 1) - (x^2 + 3x - 1) \\
&= 2hx + (h^2 + 3h).
\end{aligned}
$$

EXAMPLE 3.   Given the set of functional values $y_0 = -1$, $y_1 = 0$, $y_2 = 5$, $y_3 = 20$, express y_3 in terms of the leading term and leading differences and evaluate.

Solution: Difference Table B is constructed for the given data.

Difference Table B

y	Δy	$\Delta^2 y$	$\Delta^3 y$
-1			
	1		
0		4	
	5		6
5		10	
	15		
20			

The leading term is $y_0 = -1$ and the leading differences are $\Delta y_0 = 1$, $\Delta^2 y_0 = 4$, and $\Delta^3 y_0 = 6$. Applying equation (1.14),

$$y_3 = y_0 + \binom{3}{1}\Delta y_0 + \binom{3}{2}\Delta^2 y_0 + \binom{3}{3}\Delta^3 y_0.$$

Substituting the values of the leading term and leading differences,

$$y_3 = (-1) + 3(1) + 3(4) + (6)$$
$$= -1 + 3 + 12 + 6$$
$$= 20.$$

The result agrees with the given data.

Other important operators will be discussed later in our work on finite differences. However, we now make brief mention of two interesting operators. It follows from the definition of the shift operator that

$$E^m[E^n f(x)] = E^{m+n} f(x).$$

Making use of this property, we are able to define the *inverse operator* E^{-1}. Now,

$$E[E^{-1} f(x)] = f(x).$$

Hence,

$$E^{-1} f(x) = f(x - h), \qquad \textbf{1.15}$$

and, in general,

$$E^{-n} f(x) = f(x - nh). \qquad \textbf{1.16}$$

A second operator of interest is the *backward difference operator* ∇ defined by

$$\nabla f(x) = f(x) - f(x - h). \qquad \textbf{1.17}$$

Making use of equations (1.15) and (1.17), we may write

$$\nabla f(x) = (1 - E^{-1}) f(x). \qquad \textbf{1.18}$$

Higher-order backward differences are defined in an analogous manner to higher-order *forward* differences. Hence, we may show that

$$\nabla^n f(x) = f(x) - \binom{n}{1} f(x - h) + \binom{n}{2} f(x - 2h) - \cdots + (-1)^n f(x - nh).$$

$$\textbf{1.19}$$

EXERCISES

1. Find the following where the unit of increment for the independent variable is $h = 1$:

   (a) Δx^3;

   (b) $\Delta^3 ax^3$;

   (c) Δa^x;

   (d) $\Delta^n a^x$;

   (e) Δe^x;

   (f) $\Delta \binom{x}{3}$;

   (g) $\Delta x!$;

   (h) $\Delta \sin x$;

   (i) $\Delta \dfrac{1}{(x+1)(x+2)(x+3)}$;

   (j) $\Delta x3^x$;

   (k) Ex^4;

   (l) $E^2 x!$;

   (m) $E \cos x$;

   (n) $E \binom{x}{r}$;

   (o) $E \dfrac{1}{x(x+1)}$;

   (p) $E^n e^x$;

   (q) ∇x^2;

   (r) $\nabla \dfrac{1}{x(x+1)(x+2)}$;

   (s) $E^{-1} 3x^2$;

   (t) $E^{-n} x$.

2. Find $\Delta^2 f(x)$ for $f(x) = ax^2 + bx + c$ with $h = 2$.

3. Find the value of $\dfrac{\Delta^3 x!}{x!}$ for $x = 9$ with $h = 1$.

4. Find $E^3(ax^2 + bx + c)$ using equation (1.10) with $h = 1$.

5. Find $\Delta^k \binom{x}{r}$ for $k < r$ with $h = 1$.

6. Consider a set of points (t_0, y_0), (t_1, y_1), $\ldots$, (t_n, y_n), where $t_{i+1} - t_i = h$. Obtain by a transformation of variables, $t = hx$, a corresponding set of points (x_0, y_0), (x_1, y_1), $\ldots$, (x_n, y_n). Show that $x_{i+1} - x_i = 1$.

7. Prove that:

   (a) $y_5 = y_4 + \Delta y_3 + \Delta^2 y_2 + \Delta^3 y_2$

   (b) $y_3 = y_1 + 2\Delta y_1 + \Delta^2 y_0 + \Delta^3 y_0$

   (c) $y_4 = y_2 + 2\Delta y_2 + \Delta^2 y_1 + \Delta^3 y_0 + \Delta^4 y_0$

8. Find y_{12} if $y_0 = 1$, $y_1 = 12$, $y_2 = 38$, $y_3 = 84$, and $y_4 = 155$. What assumption is made?

9. Find y_{-2} if $y_0 = 5$, $y_1 = 8$, $y_2 = 11$, and $y_3 = 14$. What assumption is made?

10. Express y_i in terms of y_2 and its higher-order differences.

11. Derive equation (1.9) by means of mathematical induction.

12. Given the set of points $(0, 1)$, $(1, 3)$, $(2, 9)$, $(3, 16)$, and $(4, 19)$, find:

    (a) $E^{-3} y_4$

    (b) $\left(1 - \dfrac{\Delta}{E}\right)^{-1} y_3$

    (c) $\dfrac{\Delta^2}{E} y_2$

4. DIFFERENCE THEOREMS

Consider a general third degree polynomial function $y = ax^3 + bx^2 + cx + d$. Table 1.3 is a diagonal difference table for such a function with initial value of

TABLE 1.3

x	y	Δy	$\Delta^2 y$	$\Delta^3 y$
0	d			
		$(ah^3 + bh^2 + ch)$		
h	$(ah^3 + bh^2 + ch + d)$		$(6ah^3 + 2bh^2)$	
		$(7ah^3 + 3bh^2 + ch)$		$(6ah^3)$
$2h$	$(8ah^3 + 4bh^2 + 2ch + d)$		$(12ah^3 + 2bh^2)$	
		$(19ah^3 + 5bh^2 + ch)$		$(6ah^3)$
$3h$	$(27ah^3 + 9bh^2 + 3ch + d)$		$(18ah^3 + 2bh^2)$	
		$(37ah^3 + 7bh^2 + ch)$		$(6ah^3)$
$4h$	$(64ah^3 + 16bh^2 + 4ch + d)$		$(24ah^3 + 2bh^2)$	
		$(61ah^3 + 9bh^2 + ch)$		
$5h$	$(125ah^3 + 25bh^2 + 5ch + d)$			

the independent variable equal to zero and unit increments of h (not necessarily unity). The fact that the third differences are all constant is not a coincidence. In fact, it may be shown that, in general, if $f(x)$ is a polynomial of the nth degree, then the nth differences of the function are constant. In order to prove this theorem, we need to derive several preliminary theorems and rules. The theorems to be derived are formulas which enable differences to be taken. Rules, on the other hand, shall denote relationships concerning differences of one or more functions.

Rule I.   *Distributive Rule.* $\Delta[f(x) + g(x)] = \Delta f(x) + \Delta g(x)$.

$$\begin{aligned} Proof: \quad \Delta[f(x) + g(x)] &= [f(x + h) + g(x + h)] - [f(x) + g(x)] \\ &= [f(x + h) - f(x)] + [g(x + h) - g(x)] \\ &= \Delta f(x) + \Delta g(x). \end{aligned}$$

By means of mathematical induction, we may show that

$$\Delta[f_1(x) + f_2(x) + \cdots + f_n(x)] = \Delta f_1(x) + \Delta f_2(x) + \cdots + \Delta f_n(x)$$

or, in more concise notation,

$$\Delta \sum_{i=1}^{n} f_i(x) = \sum_{i=1}^{n} \Delta f_i(x).$$

The proof of this statement is left for the student as an exercise.
In a similar fashion,

$$E[f_1(x) + f_2(x) + \cdots + f_n(x)] = Ef_1(x) + Ef_2(x) + \cdots + Ef_n(x);$$

that is,

$$E \sum_{i=1}^{n} f_i(x) = \sum_{i=1}^{n} Ef_i(x).$$

Rule 2.   *Commutative Rule.* $\Delta cf(x) = c\Delta f(x)$ for every constant c.

Proof:
$$\Delta cf(x) = cf(x + h) - cf(x)$$
$$= c[f(x + h) - f(x)]$$
$$= c\Delta f(x).$$

In general, it may be shown by mathematical induction that
$$\Delta^n cf(x) = c\Delta^n f(x).$$

In a similar fashion,
$$E^n cf(x) = cE^n f(x).$$

Rule 3.   *Rule of Exponents.* $\Delta^m[\Delta^n f(x)] = \Delta^{m+n} f(x)$.

Proof: From the definition of higher-order differences, with the subscripts indicating the number of differences taken,
$$\Delta^m[\Delta^n f(x)] = (\Delta_1\Delta_2 \cdots \Delta_m)[(\Delta_1\Delta_2 \cdots \Delta_n)f(x)]$$
$$= (\Delta_1\Delta_2 \cdots \Delta_{m+n})f(x)$$
$$= \Delta^{m+n} f(x).$$

In a similar fashion,
$$E^m[E^n f(x)] = E^{m+n} f(x).$$

Notice that these rules concern difference relationships, but do not enable us actually to find differences of functions. The following theorems will help us accomplish this objective in a limited fashion. Other useful formulas will appear later in our study. We shall assume $h = 1$ for the derivation of the theorems which follow. The generalizations of these theorems for any value of h will be left as exercises for the student.

Theorem 1. $\Delta c = 0$, *where c is a constant.*

Proof: $\Delta c = c - c = 0$.

Theorem 2. $\Delta x^n = p(x)$, *where $p(x)$ is a polynomial of degree $n - 1$ with leading term nx^{n-1}.*

Proof: $\Delta x^n = (x + 1)^n - x^n$
$$= x^n + \binom{n}{1}x^{n-1} + \binom{n}{2}x^{n-2} + \cdots + \binom{n}{i}x^{n-i} + \cdots + 1 - x^n$$
$$= \binom{n}{1}x^{n-1} + \binom{n}{2}x^{n-2} + \cdots + \binom{n}{i}x^{n-i} + \cdots + 1$$
$$= \sum_{i=1}^{n} \binom{n}{i}x^{n-i}, \quad \text{a polynomial of } (n-1)\text{th degree with leading term } nx^{n-1}.$$

Theorem 3. $\Delta^n x^n = n!$.

The proof follows by successive applications of the previously proven rules and theorems.

Theorem 4. $\Delta^n cx^n = cn!$

$$\begin{aligned}
\textit{Proof:} \quad \Delta^n cx^n &= c\Delta^n x^n && \text{by Rule 2,} \\
&= cn! && \text{by Theorem 3.}
\end{aligned}$$

Theorem 5. $\Delta^{n+1} x^n = 0$.

$$\begin{aligned}
\textit{Proof:} \quad \Delta^{n+1} x^n &= \Delta(\Delta^n x^n) && \text{by Rule 3,} \\
&= \Delta n! && \text{by Theorem 3,} \\
&= 0 && \text{by Theorem 1.}
\end{aligned}$$

Extending Theorem 5, we have

$$\Delta^{n+i} x^n = 0 \text{ for } i = 1, 2, 3, \ldots.$$

Theorem 6.   *If* $p(x) = a_0 x^n + a_1 x^{n-1} + \cdots + a_i x^{n-i} + \cdots + a_n$, *then* $\Delta^n p(x) = a_0 n!$.

   Proof:

$$\begin{aligned}
\Delta^n p(x) &= \Delta^n [a_0 x^n + a_1 x^{n-1} + \cdots + a_i x^{n-i} + \cdots + a_n] \\
&= \Delta^n a_0 x^n + \Delta^n a_1 x^{n-1} + \cdots + \Delta^n a_i x^{n-i} + \cdots + \Delta^n a_n \quad \text{by Rule 1,} \\
&= a_0 \Delta^n x^n + a_1 \Delta^n x^{n-1} + \cdots + a_i \Delta^n x^{n-i} + \cdots + \Delta^n a_n \quad \text{by Rule 2,} \\
&= a_0 \Delta^n x^n \quad \text{by Theorems 1 and 5,} \\
&= a_0 n! \quad \text{by Theorem 3.}
\end{aligned}$$

Hence, we have shown that the nth-order difference of an nth degree polynomial function is a constant. It follows that higher-order differences of the same polynomial function vanish.

5. TABULAR ERRORS

Quite often a diagonal difference table may be employed to determine the validity of a table of functional values. Consider $y_0, y_1, y_2, \ldots, y_n$ to be the true values of a function and let the reading for y_4 be in error by an amount ϵ.

Table 1.4 illustrates the manner in which the error is propagated with regard to the higher-order differences.

TABLE I.4

y	Δy	$\Delta^2 y$	$\Delta^3 y$	$\Delta^4 y$
y_0				
	Δy_0			
y_1		$\Delta^2 y_0$		
	Δy_1		$\Delta^3 y_0$	
y_2		$\Delta^2 y_1$		$\Delta^4 y_0 + \epsilon$
	Δy_2		$\Delta^3 y_1 + \epsilon$	
y_3		$\Delta^2 y_2 + \epsilon$		$\Delta^4 y_1 - 4\epsilon$
	$\Delta y_3 + \epsilon$		$\Delta^3 y_2 - 3\epsilon$	
$y_4 + \epsilon$		$\Delta^2 y_3 - 2\epsilon$		$\Delta^4 y_2 + 6\epsilon$
	$\Delta y_4 - \epsilon$		$\Delta^3 y_3 + 3\epsilon$	
y_5		$\Delta^2 y_4 + \epsilon$		$\Delta^4 y_3 - 4\epsilon$
	Δy_5		$\Delta^3 y_4 - \epsilon$	
y_6		$\Delta^2 y_5$		$\Delta^4 y_4 + \epsilon$
	Δy_6		$\Delta^3 y_5$	
y_7		$\Delta^2 y_6$		
	Δy_7			
y_8				

It should be noted that the effect of the error increases with the order of the differences. Furthermore, the error table exhibits the following properties:

1. The coefficients of the ϵ's in the nth difference column are the nth-order binomial coefficients with alternating signs.

2. The algebraic sum of the ϵ's in any difference column is zero.

3. The maximum error in each difference column is in the same horizontal line as the incorrect tabular value or in the lines directly above and below that horizontal line.

These properties of the error table enable us, generally, to locate and correct the source of an error in one of the original functional values. If more than one functional value is in error, the process becomes complicated. In addition to the usefulness of this method in checking tables of functional values given by known functions, it may be employed to locate errors in experimental data.

EXAMPLE. Find the error in the tabulated functional values whose difference table is shown in Difference Table C.

Difference Table C

x	y	Δy	$\Delta^2 y$	$\Delta^3 y$	$\Delta^4 y$
0	1				
		-3			
1	-2		-2		
		-5		6	
2	-7		4		3
		-1		9	
3	-8		13		-12
		12		-3	
4	4		10		18
		22		15	
5	26		25		-12
		47		3	
6	73		28		3
		75		6	
7	148		34		
		109			
8	257				

Solution: Now, the fourth difference column contains values with alternating signs symmetrically placed about a horizontal line through y_4. Assuming the error to be contained in y_4 and fourth differences constant, we have

$$3 = \Delta^4 y_0 + \epsilon,$$
$$-12 = \Delta^4 y_1 - 4\epsilon,$$
$$18 = \Delta^4 y_2 + 6\epsilon,$$
$$-12 = \Delta^4 y_3 - 4\epsilon,$$
$$3 = \Delta^4 y_4 + \epsilon,$$

with $\Delta^4 y_0 = \Delta^4 y_1 = \Delta^4 y_2 = \Delta^4 y_3 = \Delta^4 y_4$. Hence, taking the first two equations above and equating $\Delta^4 y_0$ and $\Delta^4 y_1$,

$$3 - \epsilon = -12 + 4\epsilon,$$
$$5\epsilon = 15,$$
$$\epsilon = 3.$$

Now, $y_4 + \epsilon = 4$. Hence, $y_4 = 1$.

EXERCISES

1. Derive the generalized form of Rule 1 for n functions by means of mathematical induction.
2. Prove that $\Delta^n cf(x) = c\Delta^n f(x)$ by means of mathematical induction.
3. Prove three rules analogous to Rules 1, 2, and 3, respectively, for the shift operator E.
4. Find $\Delta^n x^n$ where h is the unit of increment of the independent variable.
5. Find $\Delta^n p(x)$ where $p(x)$ is a polynomial of the form $a_0 x^n + a_1 x^{n-1} + \cdots + a_n$ with h the unit of increment of the independent variable.
6. Verify Theorem 6 for the following functions:
   (a) x^4
   (b) $2x^3 - 3x^2 + x + 5$
   (c) $ax^2 + bx + c$
7. Verify the results of Exercise 5 for the functions of Exercise 6.
8. Determine the degree of the polynomial y_x if

$$y_k = y_{k-1} + y_{k-3} - y_{k-4}.$$

9. Find $\Delta^6[(1 + x)(1 + ax)^2(1 + bx)^3]$.
10. Find functions whose first differences are given, let $h = 1$:
    (a) x
    (b) $x + 3$
    (c) $2x^2 - 3x + 4$
11. Given the following data, find and correct a likely random error:

(a)

x	0	1	2	3	4	5
y	-21	-16	-7	0	11	24

(b)

x	0	1	2	3	4	5	6	7	8
y	0	-9	-12	-3	24	57	156	273	432

(c)

x	0	1	2	3	4	5	6	7
y	12	10	24	24	40	62	90	124

2

Interpolation

I. NEWTON'S BINOMIAL INTERPOLATION FORMULA

Given a set of $n + 1$ equally spaced points $(x_0, y_0), (x_1, y_1), \ldots, (x_n, y_n)$, equation (1.14) expresses a relationship for every value of the dependent variable in terms of the leading term and leading differences. Its derivation depended upon the symbolic relationship

$$E^n = (1 + \Delta)^n \qquad \qquad \textbf{2.1}$$

for positive integral values of n.

Consider equation (1.14) with $i = x$, $x_0 = 0$, and $h = 1$. Then

$$I(x) = y_0 + \binom{x}{1}\Delta y_0 + \binom{x}{2}\Delta^2 y_0 + \cdots + \binom{x}{n}\Delta^n y_0. \qquad \textbf{2.2}$$

Equation (2.2) obviously is satisfied by the $n + 1$ points $(x_0, y_0), (x_1, y_1), \ldots, (x_n, y_n)$ since equation (1.14) is satisfied by the points. In addition, the equation represents a polynomial of degree n or less. Hence, equation (2.2) may be considered as representing an interpolation function $I(x)$ for the given set of data under the criterion $I(x_i) = y_i$.

Equation (2.2) is valid for all values of $x \neq x_i$ under the assumption that the polynomial function $I(x)$ generated the data. This is equivalent to assuming equation (2.1) valid for all real n. Care must be taken to accept equation (2.1) as true for only the positive integers when the relationship expressed is applied to other functional forms.

The formula represented by equation (2.2) is called *Newton's Binomial Interpolation Formula*. It is one of the best known of the classical interpolation formulas. Newton's Binomial Interpolation Formula is the fundamental formula for the interpolation and the extrapolation of data with equal increments of the independent variable. In the next section we shall consider the case of equal increments not equal to unity.

EXAMPLE. Determine an interpolation polynomial $I(x)$ for the points $(0, -2)$, $(1, 5)$, $(2, 7)$, and $(3, 10)$ such that $I(x_i) = y_i$.

Solution: Since $x_0 = 0$ and $x_{i+1} - x_i = 1$, we may employ Newton's Binomial Interpolation Formula to determine an interpolation polynomial passing through the given points. Difference Table A is constructed for the given data.

Difference Table A

x	y	Δy	$\Delta^2 y$	$\Delta^3 y$
0	-2			
		7		
1	5		-5	
		2		6
2	7		1	
		3		
3	10			

Now, $y_0 = -2$, $\Delta y_0 = 7$, $\Delta^2 y_0 = -5$, and $\Delta^3 y_0 = 6$. Hence, by equation (2.2),

$$I(x) = -2 + 7\binom{x}{1} - 5\binom{x}{2} + 6\binom{x}{3}$$

$$= -2 + 7x - \tfrac{5}{2}x(x-1) + x(x-1)(x-2)$$

$$= x^3 - \tfrac{11}{2}x^2 + \tfrac{23}{2}x - 2.$$

2. TRANSFORMATION OF VARIABLES

If $I(x)$ of equation (2.2) is to represent a polynomial function of the real variable x which fits the given $n + 1$ points $(x_0, y_0), (x_1, y_1), \ldots, (x_n, y_n)$, then x_0 must, of necessity, be zero and h must equal 1 in order that each x_i correspond to a real positive integer i. Obviously, neither of these two conditions needs to hold in order to obtain a polynomial expression for a given set of $n + 1$ points. We now propose to examine the change in Newton's Binomial Interpolation Formula if both conditions are relaxed.

Consider the situation where $x_0 = k$ and $h \neq 1$. A transformation of variables of the form

$$r = \frac{x - x_0}{h} \qquad\qquad \textbf{2.3}$$

transforms the set of points $(x_0, y_0), (x_1, y_1), \ldots, (x_n, y_n)$ to a set of points $(r_0, y_0), (r_1, y_1), \ldots, (r_n, y_n)$, respectively, which has the following desired properties:

1. $r_0 = 0$ 2. $r_{i+1} - r_i = 1$ 3. $r_i = i$

Hence, by application of equation (2.2),

$$I(r) = y_0 + \binom{r}{1}\Delta y_0 + \binom{r}{2}\Delta^2 y_0 + \cdots + \binom{r}{n}\Delta^n y_0. \qquad \textbf{2.4}$$

A substitution for r in terms of the original variable x yields

$$I(x) = y_0 + \binom{\dfrac{x - x_0}{h}}{1}\Delta y_0 + \binom{\dfrac{x - x_0}{h}}{2}\Delta^2 y_0 + \cdots + \binom{\dfrac{x - x_0}{h}}{n}\Delta^n y_0. \qquad \textbf{2.5}$$

Careful note should be made that y_0 is the functional value corresponding to x_0, not to $x = 0$. Equation (2.5) represents the most general form of Newton's Binomial Interpolation Formula. However, it is important to remember that a transformation of variable is always possible which will enable us to consider an independent variable with unit increments and initial value zero. Hence, either equation (2.2) or (2.4) may be said to represent the basic form of Newton's Binomial Interpolation Formula.

If, however, the data are not given in terms of equally spaced values of x, regardless of the initial value of x, we are not able to apply the methods developed thus far to the problem of obtaining an interpolation function. In a later section, a new operator will be introduced which will enable us to handle such cases with a reasonable amount of labor.

EXAMPLE.   Determine an interpolation polynomial $I(x)$ for the points $(-3, 17)$, $(-1, 9)$, $(1, 1)$, $(3, 41)$, and $(5, 177)$ such that $I(x_i) = y_i$.

Solution: Now, $x_0 \neq 0$. However, since $x_{i+1} - x_i = 2$, we may employ a transformation of variables.

Let

$$r = \frac{x - x_0}{x_{i+1} - x_i} = \frac{x + 3}{2}.$$

Then our given points are made to correspond to the points $(0, 17)$, $(1, 9)$, $(2, 1)$, $(3, 41)$, and $(4, 177)$. A difference table for the new data appears as Difference Table B.

Difference Table B

r	y	Δy	$\Delta^2 y$	$\Delta^3 y$
0	17			
		-8		
1	9		0	
		-8		48
2	1		48	
		40		48
3	41		96	
		136		
4	177			

The leading term and leading differences are 17, -8, 0, and 48. Applying equation (2.4),

$$I(r) = 17 - 8\binom{r}{1} + 48\binom{r}{3}$$

$$= 17 - 8r + 8r(r-1)(r-2)$$

$$= 8r^3 - 24r^2 + 8r + 17.$$

Since $r = \dfrac{x+3}{2}$, the interpolation polynomial for the given data in original form becomes

$$I(x) = 8\left(\frac{x+3}{2}\right)^3 - 24\left(\frac{x+3}{2}\right)^2 + 8\left(\frac{x+3}{2}\right) + 17$$

$$= (x+3)^3 - 6(x+3)^2 + 4(x+3) + 17$$

$$= x^3 + 3x^2 - 5x + 2.$$

EXERCISES

1. Derive Newton's Binomial Interpolation Formula by the use of mathematical induction.

2. Find interpolation polynomials for the following sets of data such that $I(x_i) = y_i$:

(a)

x	0	1	2	3	4
y	5	3	7	47	177

(b)

x	-3	0	3	6
y	19	1	1	19

(c)

x	0	2	4	6
y	3	3	51	195

(d)

x	3	4	5	6	7	8
y	-4	-2	2	14	40	86

(e)

x	-0.4	-0.2	0	0.2	0.4
y	-2	2	0	-2	2

3. Using a table of values for $\sin 10°$, $\sin 20°$, $\sin 30°$, and $\sin 40°$, find an approximation for $\sin 33°$ by means of Newton's Binomial Interpolation Formula.

4. Using a table of values for the $\log 255$, $\log 261$, $\log 267$, and $\log 273$, find an approximation for $\log 285$.

5. Express equation (2.2) if $x_0 = 2$ and $h = 1$.

6. Expand the first four terms of equation (2.5).

7. Show that any two of the three stated desirable properties of the transformation defined by equation (2.3) implies the third.

3. LAGRANGE'S INTERPOLATION FORMULA

The problem of determining an interpolation polynomial for a set of $n + 1$ points $(x_0, y_0), (x_1, y_1), \ldots, (x_n, y_n)$ where $x_{i+1} - x_i$ is *not constant* is extremely important. Many times it is inconvenient, if not impossible, to collect empirical data equally spaced with regard to the independent variable. Under the criterion $I(x_i) = y_i$, a formula known as Lagrange's Interpolation Formula is of considerable theoretical value.

Let $n + 1$ points $(x_0, y_0), (x_1, y_1), \ldots, (x_n, y_n)$ be given. Now, it is always possible to determine a polynomial of degree n, or less, which passes through the $n + 1$ points. Consider the polynomial

$$
\begin{aligned}
I(x) = {} & c_0(x - x_1)(x - x_2)(x - x_3) \cdots (x - x_n) \\
& + c_1(x - x_0)(x - x_2)(x - x_3) \cdots (x - x_n) \\
& + c_2(x - x_0)(x - x_1)(x - x_3) \cdots (x - x_n) \\
& + \cdots \\
& + c_n(x - x_0)(x - x_1)(x - x_2) \cdots (x - x_{n-1}).
\end{aligned}
\qquad \textbf{2.6}
$$

Since each term of the polynomial $I(x)$ is itself a polynomial of the nth degree, $I(x)$ is a polynomial of the nth degree. If $I(x)$ is to represent the given data such that $I(x_i) = y_i$, it remains for us to examine the conditions placed upon the c_i's. We shall determine the $n + 1$ constants c_i by substituting the $n + 1$ given pairs of values. Now,

$$
I(x_0) = y_0 = c_0(x_0 - x_1)(x_0 - x_2)(x_0 - x_3) \cdots (x_0 - x_n).
$$

Hence,

$$
c_0 = \frac{y_0}{(x_0 - x_1)(x_0 - x_2)(x_0 - x_3) \cdots (x_0 - x_n)}.
$$

Similarly,

$$
c_1 = \frac{y_1}{(x_1 - x_0)(x_1 - x_2)(x_1 - x_3) \cdots (x_1 - x_n)};
$$

$$
c_2 = \frac{y_2}{(x_2 - x_0)(x_2 - x_1)(x_2 - x_3) \cdots (x_2 - x_n)};
$$

$$
\vdots
$$

$$
c_n = \frac{y_n}{(x_n - x_0)(x_n - x_1)(x_n - x_2) \cdots (x_n - x_{n-1})}.
$$

That is, in general,

$$c_i = \frac{y_i}{(x_i - x_0)(x_i - x_1) \cdots (x_i - x_{i-1})(x_i - x_{i+1}) \cdots (x_i - x_n)}. \qquad \textbf{2.7}$$

Substituting in equation (2.6) the results of equation (2.7) for $i = 0, 1, \ldots, n$, we obtain *Lagrange's Interpolation Formula:*

$$
\begin{aligned}
I(x) = &\frac{(x - x_1)(x - x_2)(x - x_3) \cdots (x - x_n)}{(x_0 - x_1)(x_0 - x_2)(x_0 - x_3) \cdots (x_0 - x_n)} y_0 \\
&+ \frac{(x - x_0)(x - x_2)(x - x_3) \cdots (x - x_n)}{(x_1 - x_0)(x_1 - x_2)(x_1 - x_3) \cdots (x_1 - x_n)} y_1 \qquad \textbf{2.8} \\
&+ \cdots \\
&+ \frac{(x - x_0)(x - x_1)(x - x_2) \cdots (x - x_{n-1})}{(x_n - x_0)(x_n - x_1)(x_n - x_2) \cdots (x_n - x_{n-1})} y_n.
\end{aligned}
$$

It should be noted that equation (2.8) is also valid if $x_{i+1} - x_i$ equals a constant.

EXAMPLE 1.   Determine an interpolation polynomial for the points $(0, -3)$, $(1, 0)$, $(3, 30)$, and $(5, 132)$ such that $I(x_i) = y_i$.

Solution: Since the given data are not equally spaced with regard to the independent variable, we need to apply Lagrange's Interpolation Formula. Now,

$$x_0 = 0, \ x_1 = 1, \ x_2 = 3, \text{ and } x_3 = 5,$$

with

$$y_0 = -3, \ y_1 = 0, \ y_2 = 30, \text{ and } y_3 = 132.$$

Substituting these values in equation (2.8), we have

$$
\begin{aligned}
I(x) = &\frac{(x - 1)(x - 3)(x - 5)}{(0 - 1)(0 - 3)(0 - 5)} (-3) \\
&+ \frac{(x - 0)(x - 1)(x - 5)}{(3 - 0)(3 - 1)(3 - 5)} (30) \\
&+ \frac{(x - 0)(x - 1)(x - 3)}{(5 - 0)(5 - 1)(5 - 3)} (132).
\end{aligned}
$$

The term in Lagrange's Interpolation Formula containing the factor y_1 vanishes since $y_1 = 0$. Expanding the above,

$$I(x) = \tfrac{1}{5}(x^3 - 9x^2 + 23x - 15) - \tfrac{5}{2}(x^3 - 6x^2 + 5x) + \tfrac{33}{10}(x^3 - 4x^2 + 3x)$$

$$= x^3 + 2x - 3.$$

EXAMPLE 2. Determine an interpolation polynomial for the points $(-2, -5a)$, $(0, a)$, and $(1, 4a)$ such that $I(x_i) = y_i$.

Solution: Applying equation (2.8) with

$x_0 = -2, y_0 = -5a, x_1 = 0, y_1 = a, x_2 = 1, \text{ and } y_2 = 4a,$

$$I(x) = \frac{(x - 0)(x - 1)}{(-2 - 0)(-2 - 1)}(-5a) + \frac{(x + 2)(x - 1)}{(0 + 2)(0 - 1)}(a) + \frac{(x + 2)(x - 0)}{(1 + 2)(1 - 0)}(4a)$$

$$= -\tfrac{5}{6}ax(x - 1) - \tfrac{1}{2}a(x + 2)(x - 1) + \tfrac{4}{3}ax(x + 2)$$

$$= -\tfrac{5}{6}ax^2 + \tfrac{5}{6}ax - \tfrac{1}{2}ax^2 - \tfrac{1}{2}ax + a + \tfrac{4}{3}ax^2 + \tfrac{8}{3}ax$$

$$= 3ax + a.$$

EXERCISES

1. Find interpolation polynomials for the following sets of data such that $I(x_i) = y_i$:

(a)

x	−1	0	2
y	9	5	3

(b)

x	0	1	3
y	10	12	−8

(c)

x	−2	−1	0	2
y	−3	6	5	−3

(d)

x	−2	0	1	3
y	9	5	6	14

(e)

x	2	3	6	12
y	15	18	30	60

2. Find an approximation for $\cos 53°$ making use of the values for $\cos 30°$, $\cos 45°$, and $\cos 60°$.

3. Show that the coefficients of the y_i's in Lagrange's Interpolation Formula are invariant under a transformation of variables $x = aw + b$, where a and b are constants.

4. Making use of the results of Exercise 3, find the coefficients in Lagrange's Interpolation Formula for the following set of values of the independent variable:

$$x = -0.5, 1.0, 2.5, 4.0, 5.5.$$

5. Given the data

x	0	1	2	3
y	y_0	y_1	y_2	y_3

$y_{1/2}$ is evaluated by means of Lagrange's Interpolation Formula. It is then discovered that y_1 is 1.4 units too large. What is the error in $y_{1/2}$?

6. Show that the coefficient of y_i in Lagrange's Interpolation Formula may be expressed as:

$$\frac{\displaystyle\prod_{j=0}^{n}(x - x_j)}{(x - x_i)\dfrac{d}{dx}\left[\displaystyle\prod_{j=0}^{n}(x - x_j)\right]_{x_i}}.$$

7. Making use of the results of Exercise 6, show that Lagrange's Interpolation Formula may be written in the form:

$$I(x) = \prod_{j=0}^{n}(x - x_j)\sum_{i=0}^{n}\frac{y_i}{(x - x_i)\dfrac{d}{dx}\left[\displaystyle\prod_{j=0}^{n}(x - x_j)\right]_{x_i}}.$$

8. Discuss the results of Exercise 7 if the values of x are equally spaced.

4. DIVIDED DIFFERENCES

The solution of the problem of determining an interpolation function for a set of data unequally spaced with respect to the independent variable may be facilitated by the introduction of a new differencing operation. Consider a set of $n + 1$ points $(x_0, y_0), (x_1, y_1), \ldots, (x_n, y_n)$. We shall define the *first-order divided difference* of a pair of successive points (x_i, y_i) and (x_{i+1}, y_{i+1}) as

$$\frac{y_{i+1} - y_i}{x_{i+1} - x_i}$$

and shall denote such a difference by the notation

$$\Delta[x_{i+1}x_i].$$

That is,

$$\Delta[x_{i+1}x_i] = \frac{y_{i+1} - y_i}{x_{i+1} - x_i}. \qquad \textbf{2.9}$$

It should be noted that since

$$\Delta[x_i x_{i+1}] = \frac{y_i - y_{i+1}}{x_i - x_{i+1}} = \frac{y_{i+1} - y_i}{x_{i+1} - x_i},$$

then

$$\Delta[x_{i+1}x_i] = \Delta[x_i x_{i+1}]. \qquad \textbf{2.10}$$

Therefore, the order of the factors within the brackets is immaterial.

Higher-order divided differences are defined in a manner somewhat analogous to our defining of higher-order ordinary differences. We shall define the *second-order divided difference* as the quotient of the difference of two adjacent first-order divided differences and the difference of the two extreme x_i's involved in calculating the first-order divided differences; that is,

$$\frac{\Delta[x_{i+2}x_{i+1}] - \Delta[x_{i+1}x_i]}{x_{i+2} - x_i}.$$

We shall denote the general second-order divided difference by $\Delta^2[x_{i+2}x_i]$. Therefore,

$$\Delta^2[x_{i+2}x_i] = \frac{\Delta[x_{i+2}x_{i+1}] - \Delta[x_{i+1}x_i]}{x_{i+2} - x_i}. \qquad \textbf{2.11}$$

In general, the *nth-order divided difference* shall be denoted by

$$\Delta^n[x_n x_0]$$

and defined by

$$\Delta^n[x_n x_0] = \frac{\Delta^{n-1}[x_n x_1] - \Delta^{n-1}[x_{n-1} x_0]}{x_n - x_0}. \qquad \textbf{2.12}$$

A diagonal divided difference table for the $n + 1$ points (x_0, y_0), (x_1, y_1), ..., (x_n, y_n) is of the form

x_0	y_0				
		$\Delta[x_1 x_0]$			
x_1	y_1		$\Delta^2[x_2 x_0]$		
		$\Delta[x_2 x_1]$		$\Delta^3[x_3 x_0]$	
x_2	y_2		$\Delta^2[x_3 x_1]$	.	.
		$\Delta[x_3 x_2]$	.	.	$\Delta^n[x_n x_0]$
x_3	y_3	.	.	.	
.	.	.	.	$\Delta^3[x_n x_{n-3}]$	
.	.	.	$\Delta^2[x_n x_{n-2}]$		
.	.	$\Delta[x_n x_{n-1}]$			
x_n	y_n				

The value of each entry in the body of the table is found by dividing the difference between the two adjacent entries in the column to the left by the difference of the two extreme x_i's involved in these entries.

As in the case of ordinary differences, every divided difference may be expressed entirely in terms of the original x_i's and y_i's. It is obvious from equation (2.9) that

$$\Delta[x_{i+1}x_i] = \frac{y_{i+1}}{x_{i+1} - x_i} + \frac{y_i}{x_i - x_{i+1}}. \qquad \textbf{2.13}$$

Now,

$$\Delta^2[x_{i+2}x_i] = \frac{\Delta[x_{i+2}x_{i+1}] - \Delta[x_{i+1}x_i]}{x_{i+2} - x_i}$$

$$= \frac{1}{x_{i+2} - x_i}\left(\frac{y_{i+2} - y_{i+1}}{x_{i+2} - x_{i+1}} - \frac{y_{i+1} - y_i}{x_{i+1} - x_i}\right).$$

Hence,

$$\Delta^2[x_{i+2}x_i] = \frac{y_{i+2}}{(x_{i+2} - x_i)(x_{i+2} - x_{i+1})} + \frac{y_{i+1}}{(x_{i+1} - x_i)(x_{i+1} - x_{i+2})}$$

$$+ \frac{y_i}{(x_i - x_{i+1})(x_i - x_{i+2})}. \qquad \textbf{2.14}$$

Similarly,

$$\Delta^3[x_{i+3}x_i] = \frac{y_{i+3}}{(x_{i+3} - x_i)(x_{i+3} - x_{i+1})(x_{i+3} - x_{i+2})}$$

$$+ \frac{y_{i+2}}{(x_{i+2} - x_i)(x_{i+2} - x_{i+1})(x_{i+2} - x_{i+3})}$$

$$+ \frac{y_{i+1}}{(x_{i+1} - x_i)(x_{i+1} - x_{i+2})(x_{i+1} - x_{i+3})}$$

$$+ \frac{y_i}{(x_i - x_{i+1})(x_i - x_{i+2})(x_i - x_{i+3})} .$$

2.15

In general, it can be shown by mathematical induction that

$$\Delta^n[x_{i+n}x_i] = \frac{y_{i+n}}{(x_{i+n} - x_i)(x_{i+n} - x_{i+1})(x_{i+n} - x_{i+2}) \cdots (x_{i+n} - x_{i+n-1})}$$

$$+ \cdots$$

$$+ \frac{y_{i+2}}{(x_{i+2} - x_i)(x_{i+2} - x_{i+1})(x_{i+2} - x_{i+3}) \cdots (x_{i+2} - x_{i+n})}$$

$$+ \frac{y_{i+1}}{(x_{i+1} - x_i)(x_{i+1} - x_{i+2})(x_{i+1} - x_{i+3}) \cdots (x_{i+1} - x_{i+n})}$$

$$+ \frac{y_i}{(x_i - x_{i+1})(x_i - x_{i+2})(x_i - x_{i+3}) \cdots (x_i - x_{i+n})} .$$

2.16

Hence, every nth-order divided difference can be expressed in a symmetric form in terms of the x_i's. It should be immediately evident that every nth-order divided difference is independent of the order of the given (x_i, y_i)'s.

It is interesting to note that equation (2.16) may be written in the following determinant form:

$$\Delta^n[x_n x_0] = \begin{vmatrix} 1 & x_0 & x_0^2 & \cdots & x_0^{n-1} & y_0 \\ 1 & x_1 & x_1^2 & \cdots & x_1^{n-1} & y_1 \\ & & & \vdots & & \\ 1 & x_n & x_n^2 & \cdots & x_n^{n-1} & y_n \\ 1 & x_0 & x_0^2 & \cdots & x_0^{n-1} & x_0^n \\ 1 & x_1 & x_1^2 & \cdots & x_1^{n-1} & x_1^n \\ & & & \vdots & & \\ 1 & x_n & x_n^2 & \cdots & x_n^{n-1} & x_n^n \end{vmatrix} .$$

2.17

We shall accept equation (2.17) without proof. The general proof requires some knowledge of the properties of Vandermonde determinants.†

For an example of equation (2.17), consider

$$\Delta^2[x_2 x_0] = \frac{\begin{vmatrix} 1 & x_0 & y_0 \\ 1 & x_1 & y_1 \\ 1 & x_2 & y_2 \\ 1 & x_0 & x_0^2 \\ 1 & x_1 & x_1^2 \\ 1 & x_2 & x_2^2 \end{vmatrix}}{}.$$

By use of the elementary properties of determinants, we have

$$\Delta^2[x_2 x_0] = \frac{y_0(x_2 - x_1) - y_1(x_2 - x_0) + y_2(x_1 - x_0)}{\begin{vmatrix} 1 & x_0 & x_0^2 \\ 0 & x_1 - x_0 & x_1^2 - x_0^2 \\ 0 & x_2 - x_0 & x_2^2 - x_0^2 \end{vmatrix}}.$$

Evaluating the determinant in the denominator by minors of the first column,

$$\Delta^2[x_2 x_0] = \frac{y_0(x_2 - x_1) - y_1(x_2 - x_0) + y_2(x_1 - x_0)}{(x_1 - x_0)(x_2^2 - x_0^2) - (x_2 - x_0)(x_1^2 - x_0^2)}$$

$$= \frac{y_0(x_2 - x_1) - y_1(x_2 - x_0) + y_2(x_1 - x_0)}{(x_1 - x_0)(x_2 - x_0)(x_2 - x_1)}$$

$$= \frac{y_0}{(x_0 - x_1)(x_0 - x_2)} + \frac{y_1}{(x_1 - x_0)(x_1 - x_2)} + \frac{y_2}{(x_2 - x_0)(x_2 - x_1)}.$$

The result is consistent with equation (2.14).

Certain rules and theorems corresponding to those derived earlier for ordinary differences may be established for divided differences in a similar manner. For example, it can be shown that the following rules are valid:

Rule 1. *The divided difference of the sum of two functions is equal to the sum of the divided differences of the two functions.*

Rule 2. *The divided difference of the product of a constant and a function is the product of the constant and the divided difference of the function.*

The proofs of these rules are left to the student as an exercise.

† A determinant having unity in each position in the first row and the elements of the ith row the $(i - 1)$th power of the corresponding unspecified elements of the second row is called a *Vandermonde determinant*.

A most important theorem concerning divided differences is the following:

Theorem.   *The nth-order divided differences of an nth degree polynomial are constant.*

Proof: Given a polynomial function of the form $y = x^n$, consider any $n + 1$ points $(x_0, y_0), (x_1, y_1), \ldots, (x_n, y_n)$ which satisfy the relationship. According to equation (2.17), the nth-order divided difference $\Delta^n[x_n x_0]$ is given by

$$\Delta^n[x_n x_0] = \frac{\begin{vmatrix} 1 & x_0 & x_0^2 & \cdots & x_0^{n-1} & y_0 \\ 1 & x_1 & x_1^2 & \cdots & x_1^{n-1} & y_1 \\ \cdot & & & & & \\ \cdot & & & & & \\ \cdot & & & & & \\ 1 & x_n & x_n^2 & \cdots & x_n^{n-1} & y_n \end{vmatrix}}{\begin{vmatrix} 1 & x_0 & x_0^2 & \cdots & x_0^{n-1} & x_0^n \\ 1 & x_1 & x_1^2 & \cdots & x_1^{n-1} & x_1^n \\ \cdot & & & & & \\ \cdot & & & & & \\ \cdot & & & & & \\ 1 & x_n & x_n^2 & \cdots & x_n^{n-1} & x_n^n \end{vmatrix}} .$$

Now, replacing each y_i in the determinant in the numerator by x_i^n, we obtain

$$\Delta^n[x_n x_0] = \frac{\begin{vmatrix} 1 & x_0 & x_0^2 & \cdots & x_0^{n-1} & x_0^n \\ 1 & x_1 & x_1^2 & \cdots & x_1^{n-1} & x_1^n \\ \cdot & & & & & \\ \cdot & & & & & \\ \cdot & & & & & \\ 1 & x_n & x_n^2 & \cdots & x_n^{n-1} & x_n^n \end{vmatrix}}{\begin{vmatrix} 1 & x_0 & x_0^2 & \cdots & x_0^{n-1} & x_0^n \\ 1 & x_1 & x_1^2 & \cdots & x_1^{n-1} & x_1^n \\ \cdot & & & & & \\ \cdot & & & & & \\ \cdot & & & & & \\ 1 & x_n & x_n^2 & \cdots & x_n^{n-1} & x_n^n \end{vmatrix}} .$$

Therefore,

$$\Delta^n[x_n x_0] = 1.$$

For every polynomial of the form $y = x^k$ where $k < n$, $\Delta^n[x_n x_0] = 0$, since replacement of each y_i in equation (2.17) by x_i^k would result in two columns of the determinant in the numerator being identical. From the above argument and application of Rules 1 and 2, it follows that the nth-order divided differences of the general nth degree polynomial $a_0 x^n + a_1 x^{n-1} + \cdots + a_n$ equal the constant a_0.

EXAMPLE 1. Construct a divided difference table for the points $(0, 35)$, $(1, 29)$, $(3, -1)$, $(5, -15)$, $(7, 35)$, and $(8, 99)$.

Solution: Labeling the points (x_0, y_0), (x_1, y_1), $\ldots$, and (x_5, y_5), respectively, we have Difference Table C.

Difference Table C

x	y	$\Delta[x_{i+1}x_i]$	$\Delta^2[x_{i+2}x_i]$	$\Delta^3[x_{i+3}x_i]$
0	35			
		$\dfrac{29-35}{1-0}=-6$		
1	29		$\dfrac{-15+6}{3-0}=-3$	
		$\dfrac{-1-29}{3-1}=-15$		$\dfrac{2+3}{5-0}=1$
3	−1		$\dfrac{-7+15}{5-1}=2$	
		$\dfrac{-15+1}{5-3}=-7$		$\dfrac{8-2}{7-1}=1$
5	−15		$\dfrac{25+7}{7-3}=8$	
		$\dfrac{35+15}{7-5}=25$		$\dfrac{13-8}{8-3}=1$
7	35		$\dfrac{64-25}{8-5}=13$	
		$\dfrac{99-35}{8-7}=64$		
8	99			

EXAMPLE 2. Using the data of Example 1, find $\Delta^2[x_3x_1]$ by means of equation (2.16).

Solution: Now, according to equation (2.16),

$$\Delta^2[x_3x_1] = \frac{y_3}{(x_3-x_1)(x_3-x_2)} + \frac{y_2}{(x_2-x_1)(x_2-x_3)} + \frac{y_1}{(x_1-x_2)(x_1-x_3)}.$$

In Example 1, x_1, x_2, and x_3 are equal to 1, 3, and 5, respectively, while y_1, y_2, and y_3 equal 29, -1, and -15, respectively. Substituting these values in the expression for $\Delta^2[x_3 x_1]$, we have

$$\Delta^2[x_3 x_1] = \frac{-15}{(5-1)(5-3)} + \frac{-1}{(3-1)(3-5)} + \frac{29}{(1-3)(1-5)}$$

$$= \frac{-15}{8} + \frac{1}{4} + \frac{29}{8}$$

$$= 2.$$

This result is consistent with the result in the difference table of Example 1.

5. NEWTON'S DIVIDED DIFFERENCE FORMULA

Having introduced the concept of divided differences, it now remains for us to derive an interpolation polynomial which employs the concept. The fundamental formula concerning divided differences is due to Newton. Consider once again the $n + 1$ points (x_0, y_0), (x_1, y_1), ..., (x_n, y_n), not necessarily equally spaced with respect to the independent variable. We have already agreed that there must exist a polynomial of the nth degree, or less, which these points satisfy. Let us write such a polynomial as the sum of products of certain factors:

$$\begin{aligned} I(x) = {}&c_0 + c_1(x - x_0) + c_2(x - x_0)(x - x_1) \\ &+ c_3(x - x_0)(x - x_1)(x - x_2) + \cdots \\ &+ c_n(x - x_0)(x - x_1)(x - x_2)\cdots(x - x_{n-1}). \end{aligned}$$ **2.18**

The polynomial of equation (2.18) is obviously of the nth degree. If this expression is to represent an interpolation function for the given data such that $I(x_i) = y_i$, then the $n + 1$ given points must satisfy the equation.

Letting $x = x_0$, we have

$$c_0 = y_0.$$ **2.19**

Letting $x = x_1$,

$$y_1 = y_0 + c_1(x_1 - x_0),$$

whereby

$$c_1 = \frac{y_1 - y_0}{x_1 - x_0};$$

that is,

$$c_1 = \Delta[x_1 x_0].$$ **2.20**

Letting $x = x_2$,

$$y_2 = y_0 + \Delta[x_1 x_0](x_2 - x_0) + c_2(x_2 - x_0)(x_2 - x_1).$$

Solving for c_2, we have

$$c_2 = \frac{y_2 - y_0 - \Delta[x_1 x_0](x_2 - x_0)}{(x_2 - x_0)(x_2 - x_1)}.$$

Now, since $y_0 = y_1 - \Delta[x_1 x_0](x_1 - x_0)$,

$$c_2 = \frac{y_2 - y_1 + \Delta[x_1 x_0](x_1 - x_0) - \Delta[x_1 x_0](x_2 - x_0)}{(x_2 - x_0)(x_2 - x_1)}$$

$$= \frac{(y_2 - y_1) + \Delta[x_1 x_0](x_1 - x_2)}{(x_2 - x_0)(x_2 - x_1)}$$

$$= \frac{\Delta[x_2 x_1] - \Delta[x_1 x_0]}{(x_2 - x_0)}.$$

Hence,

$$c_2 = \Delta^2[x_2 x_0]. \qquad \qquad 2.21$$

Proceeding in a similar fashion,

$$c_n = \Delta^n[x_n x_0]. \qquad \qquad 2.22$$

Therefore, equation (2.18) may be expressed in the following form known as *Newton's Divided Difference Formula:*

$$I(x) = y_0 + \Delta[x_1 x_0](x - x_0) + \Delta^2[x_2 x_0](x - x_0)(x - x_1)$$
$$+ \Delta^3[x_3 x_0](x - x_0)(x - x_1)(x - x_2) + \cdots \qquad 2.23$$
$$+ \Delta^n[x_n x_0](x - x_0)(x - x_1)(x - x_2) \cdots (x - x_{n-1}).$$

Newton's Divided Difference Formula is more general than his ordinary difference formula since the data need not be equally spaced with regard to the x_i's. However, if $x_{i+1} - x_i = h$, then equation (2.23) becomes Newton's Binomial Interpolation Formula, since

$$\Delta[x_1 x_0] = \frac{\Delta y_0}{h},$$

$$\Delta^2[x_2 x_0] = \frac{\Delta^2 y_0}{2! \, h^2},$$

$$\Delta^3[x_3 x_0] = \frac{\Delta^3 y_0}{3! \, h^3},$$

$$\cdot$$
$$\cdot$$
$$\cdot$$

$$\Delta^n[x_n x_0] = \frac{\Delta^n y_0}{n! \, h^n}.$$

EXAMPLE.   Find an interpolation polynomial $I(x)$ for the data of Example 1 in the previous section.

Solution: Now, $y_0 = 35$, $\Delta[x_1x_0] = -6$, $\Delta^2[x_2x_0] = -3$, and $\Delta^3[x_3x_0] = 1$ with x_0, x_1, and x_2 equal to 0, 1, and 3, respectively. Making use of Newton's Divided Difference Formula, we have

$$I(x) = y_0 + \Delta[x_1x_0](x - x_0) + \Delta^2[x_2x_0](x - x_0)(x - x_1)$$
$$+ \Delta^3[x_3x_0](x - x_0)(x - x_1)(x - x_2)$$
$$= 35 - 6x - 3x(x - 1) + x(x - 1)(x - 3)$$
$$= x^3 - 7x^2 + 35.$$

EXERCISES

1. Construct divided difference tables for the following functions at $x = -1, 0, 2, 5, 6, 10$:
   (a) x^3;   (b) $ax^2 + bx + c$;
   (c) e^x;   (d) $2x^4 - 5x^3 - x^2 + x - 3$.

2. Construct divided difference tables for the following sets of points:

(a)

x	0	1	3	4	8	10
y	10	9	25	42	170	270

(b)

x	-2.5	-1.5	1.5	2.0	3.0
y	-13.125	-1.875	1.875	6.0	24.0

(c)

x	-2	0	1	3	4
y	31	1	-5	61	229

(d)

x	0.1	0.3	0.4	0.7	0.8
y	2.4	3.2	3.6	4.8	5.2

3. Determine polynomials satisfying the data of Exercise 2.
4. Given the points $(-1, 3)$, $(0, 8)$, $(2, 36)$, $(5, -51)$, and $(6, 158)$, find $\Delta^3[x_4x_1]$ by: (a) constructing a table of divided differences; (b) use of equation (2.16); (c) use of equation (2.17).
5. Find an approximation for $\sqrt{72}$ given the following data:

x	25	36	49	64
$\sqrt{x}$	5	6	7	8

6. Given $y_0 = 3$, $y_1 = -5$, $y_2 = 7$, and $y_4 = 21$, find y_3.

7. Given $y_0 = -1$, $y_2 = 15$, and $y_4 = 13$, find y_1 and y_3.

8. Fit a polynomial to the points $(0, 6)$, $(1, 4)$, $(3, 6)$, $(4, 10)$, and $(7, 34)$ by means of:
(a) Newton's Divided Difference Formula; (b) Lagrange's Interpolation Formula; (c) the formula

$$\begin{vmatrix} x^4 & x^3 & x^2 & x & y & 1 \\ x_0^4 & x_0^3 & x_0^2 & x_0 & y_0 & 1 \\ x_1^4 & x_1^3 & x_1^2 & x_1 & y_1 & 1 \\ x_2^4 & x_2^3 & x_2^2 & x_2 & y_2 & 1 \\ x_3^4 & x_3^3 & x_3^2 & x_3 & y_3 & 1 \\ x_4^4 & x_4^3 & x_4^2 & x_4 & y_4 & 1 \end{vmatrix} = 0.$$

9. Obtain Lagrange's Interpolation Formula by setting the nth-order divided difference equal to zero.

10. Show that an interpolation function which is a rational function of the form $I(x) = \dfrac{a + bx}{c + dx}$ such that $I(x_i) = y_i$ for the points (x_1, y_1), (x_2, y_2), and (x_3, y_3) may be written as

$$I(x) = \frac{\begin{vmatrix} y_1 & x - x_1 & y_1(x - x_1) \\ y_2 & x - x_2 & y_2(x - x_2) \\ y_3 & x - x_3 & y_3(x - x_3) \end{vmatrix}}{\begin{vmatrix} 1 & x - x_1 & y_1(x - x_1) \\ 1 & x - x_2 & y_2(x - x_2) \\ 1 & x - x_3 & y_3(x - x_3) \end{vmatrix}}.$$

11. Determine an interpolation function $I(x)$ of the form stated in Exercise 10 for the points $(-2, -8)$, $(0, 4)$, and $(1, 1)$.

6. SHEPPARD'S RULES

It has been noted that divided differences are symmetric functions of the x_i's. Hence, a more general procedure than Newton's may be employed for determining the interpolation polynomial for a given set of $n + 1$ points. If convenient, the points need not be considered in order of increasing or decreasing values of x. However, when an order is chosen for calculating the c_i's in equation (2.18), the same order must be followed in introducing the x_i's in the factors which follow. The principle embodied in this procedure is the same used in deriving Newton's Divided Difference Formula.

A convenient set of rules for determining the interpolation polynomial under this principle was stated by W. F. Sheppard. These rules are often called the *zig-zag rules*, and they are as follows:

1. Start with any y_i.

2. The next term will be $\Delta[x_i x_j](x - x_i)$, where $j = i + 1$ or $i - 1$.

3. Succeeding terms will contain the product of successive higher-order divided differences and factors of the form $(x - x_k)$, where the x_k's represent values of the independent variable involved in the last preceding difference.

By means of these rules, one essentially chooses one of 2^{n-1} routes for each y_i in describing the interpolation polynomial of the nth degree.

Certain interpolation formulas obtained by taking particular *zig-zag* paths are of importance for equally spaced data. Consider choosing a path employing the term y_0, odd-order divided differences on a horizontal line between y_0 and y_1, and even-order divided differences on a horizontal line through y_0 such as exhibited in Table 2.1.

TABLE 2.1

x	y	$\Delta[x_{i+1}x_i]$	$\Delta^2[x_{i+2}x_i]$	$\Delta^3[x_{i+3}x_i]$	$\Delta^4[x_{i+4}x_i]$	$\Delta^5[x_{i+5}x_i]$	$\Delta^6[x_{i+6}x_i]$
-3	y_{-3}						
		Δy_{-3}					
-2	y_{-2}		$\dfrac{\Delta^2 y_{-3}}{2!}$				
		Δy_{-2}		$\dfrac{\Delta^3 y_{-3}}{3!}$			
-1	y_{-1}		$\dfrac{\Delta^2 y_{-2}}{2!}$		$\dfrac{\Delta^4 y_{-3}}{4!}$		
		Δy_{-1}		$\dfrac{\Delta^3 y_{-2}}{3!}$		$\dfrac{\Delta^5 y_{-3}}{5!}$	
0	y_0		$\dfrac{\Delta^2 y_{-1}}{2!}$		$\dfrac{\Delta^4 y_{-2}}{4!}$		$\dfrac{\Delta^6 y_{-3}}{6!}$
		Δy_0		$\dfrac{\Delta^3 y_{-1}}{3!}$		$\dfrac{\Delta^5 y_{-2}}{5!}$	
1	y_1		$\dfrac{\Delta^2 y_0}{2!}$		$\dfrac{\Delta^4 y_{-1}}{4!}$		
		Δy_1		$\dfrac{\Delta^3 y_0}{3!}$			
2	y_2		$\dfrac{\Delta^2 y_1}{2!}$				
		Δy_2					
3	y_3						

The interpolation formula for $I(x)$ becomes

$$y_0 + x\Delta y_0 + x(x-1)\frac{\Delta^2 y_{-1}}{2!} + x(x-1)(x+1)\frac{\Delta^3 y_{-1}}{3!}$$

$$+ x(x-1)(x+1)(x-2)\frac{\Delta^4 y_{-2}}{4!}$$

$$+ x(x-1)(x+1)(x-2)(x+2)\frac{\Delta^5 y_{-2}}{5!}$$

$$+ x(x-1)(x+1)(x-2)(x+2)(x-3)\frac{\Delta^6 y_{-3}}{6!} + \cdots ;$$

that is,

$$I(x) = y_0 + \binom{x}{1}\Delta y_0 + \binom{x}{2}\Delta^2 y_{-1} + \binom{x+1}{3}\Delta^3 y_{-1}$$

$$+ \binom{x+1}{4}\Delta^4 y_{-2} + \binom{x+2}{5}\Delta^5 y_{-2} \qquad\qquad \textbf{2.24}$$

$$+ \binom{x+2}{6}\Delta^6 y_{-3} + \cdots .$$

Equation (2.24) represents *Gauss' Forward Interpolation Formula.*

If we had chosen a similar *zig-zag* path which employed odd-order divided differences on a horizontal line between y_0 and y_{-1} rather than y_0 and y_1, we would have obtained *Gauss' Backward Interpolation Formula:*

$$I(x) = y_0 + \binom{x}{1}\Delta y_{-1} + \binom{x+1}{2}\Delta^2 y_{-1}$$

$$+ \binom{x+1}{3}\Delta^3 y_{-2} + \binom{x+2}{4}\Delta^4 y_{-2} \qquad\qquad \textbf{2.25}$$

$$+ \binom{x+2}{5}\Delta^5 y_{-3} + \binom{x+3}{6}\Delta^6 y_{-3} + \cdots .$$

The derivation of other important interpolation formulas are left as exercises for the student.

The question arises as to the usefulness of these additional interpolation formulas. For a given set of $n+1$ points, the application of every interpolation formula employing Sheppard's *zig-zag* rules results in the identical interpolation polynomial. However, when $n+1$ is extremely large, we may desire to terminate the formula at some point involving the kth difference, where $k < n$. In such an instance, functional values obtained from the various interpolation formulas will differ in the magnitude of their errors. The magnitude of the error in each case will depend upon the point at which the function is evaluated. For example, in general, Gauss' Forward Interpolation Formula will converge more rapidly than Newton's Binomial Interpolation Formula for values of the independent variable about $x = 0$. On the other hand, Newton's Binomial Interpolation Formula is generally more accurate for large positive values of the independent variable.

EXAMPLE 1. Determine an interpolation polynomial $I(x)$ for the data in Difference Table D by use of the particular *zig-zag* path indicated.

Difference Table D

x	y	$\Delta[x_{i+1}x_i]$	$\Delta^2[x_{i+2}x_i]$	$\Delta^3[x_{i+3}x_i]$
0	35			
		-6		
1	29		-3	
		-15		1
3	-1		2	
		-7		-1
5	-15		8	
		25		1
7	35		13	
		64		
8	99			

Solution: The *zig-zag* path indicated introduces the expressions y_2, $\Delta[x_2x_1]$, $\Delta^2[x_3x_1]$, and $\Delta^3[x_4x_1]$ in that order. Now, according to Sheppard's rules, the terms of our interpolation polynomial will contain the factors $(x - x_2)$, $(x - x_1)$, and $(x - x_3)$ introduced in that order. Hence,

$$
\begin{aligned}
I(x) &= y_2 + \Delta[x_2x_1](x - x_2) + \Delta^2[x_3x_1](x - x_2)(x - x_1) \\
&\quad + \Delta^3[x_4x_1](x - x_2)(x - x_1)(x - x_3) \\
&= (-1) + (-15)(x - 3) + (2)(x - 3)(x - 1) \\
&\quad + (1)(x - 3)(x - 1)(x - 5) \\
&= -1 - 15x + 45 + 2x^2 - 8x + 6 \\
&\quad + x^3 - 9x^2 + 23x - 15 \\
&= x^3 - 7x^2 + 35.
\end{aligned}
$$

This result is consistent with the results of the Example in the previous section.

EXAMPLE 2.   Determine an interpolation polynomial for the following data by means of Gauss' Forward Interpolation Formula:

x	−2	−1	0	1	2	3
y	8	−3	−2	−1	12	73

Solution: Difference Table E is an ordinary difference table for the given data.

Difference Table E

x	y	Δy	$\Delta^2 y$	$\Delta^3 y$	$\Delta^4 y$
−2	8				
		−11			
−1	−3		12		
		1		−12	
0	−2		0		24
		1		12	
1	−1		12		24
		13		36	
2	12		48		
		61			
3	73				

Now, $y_0 = -2$, $\Delta y_0 = 1$, $\Delta^2 y_{-1} = 0$, $\Delta^3 y_{-1} = 12$, and $\Delta^4 y_{-2} = 24$. Hence, by use of equation (2.24),

$$I(x) = -2 + \binom{x}{1} + 12\binom{x+1}{3} + 24\binom{x+1}{4}$$

$$= -2 + x + 2(x+1)(x)(x-1) + (x+1)(x)(x-1)(x-2)$$

$$= -2 + x + 2x^3 - 2x + x^4 - 2x^3 - x^2 + 2x$$

$$= x^4 - x^2 + x - 2.$$

EXERCISES

1. Determine the polynomial which fits the following data by three different *zig-zag* paths after constructing its divided difference table:

x	0	1	3	4	6	7
y	1	13	25	49	373	841

In Exercises 2 through 5 consider equally spaced data of the form (x_i, y_i), $(x_{i+1}, y_{i+1}), \ldots, (x_n, y_n)$, where $x_{i+1} - x_i = 1$ and $x_i = i$.

2. Derive Gauss' Backward Interpolation Formula.

3. Derive *Newton's Backward Interpolation Formula* by choosing a *zig-zag* path employing $y_0, \Delta y_{-1}, \Delta^2 y_{-2}, \Delta^3 y_{-3}, \ldots$. Discuss the usefulness of this new formula.

4. Derive *Stirling's Interpolation Formula* by taking the mean of Gauss' Forward and Backward Interpolation Formulas. Discuss the usefulness of Stirling's Interpolation Formula.

5. Derive *Bessel's Interpolation Formula* by transferring the origin of Gauss' Backward Interpolation Formula from y_0 to y_1 and taking the mean of this formula and Gauss' Forward Interpolation Formula. Discuss the usefulness of Bessel's Interpolation Formula.

6. Determine a polynomial which fits the following data by: **(a)** Newton's Binomial Interpolation Formula (often called *Newton's Forward Interpolation Formula*); **(b)** Newton's Backward Interpolation Formula; **(c)** Gauss' Forward Interpolation Formula; **(d)** Gauss' Backward Interpolation Formula; **(e)** Stirling's Interpolation Formula; and **(f)** Bessel's Interpolation Formula.

x	-2	-1	0	1	2
y	11	0	1	2	15

7. Repeat Exercise 6 neglecting third- and higher-order differences. Evaluate the resulting interpolation polynomials for $x = -2.5$, -1, -0.5, 0, 0.5, 1, and 2.5. Discuss the errors involved.

8. Define two new operators δ and μ, called the *central difference operators*, such that

$$\delta f(x) = f\left(x + \frac{h}{2}\right) - f\left(x - \frac{h}{2}\right)$$

and

$$\mu f(x) = \frac{1}{2}\left[f\left(x + \frac{h}{2}\right) + f\left(x - \frac{h}{2}\right)\right].$$

Show that:
(a) $\delta = E^{-1/2}\Delta$;
(b) $E^{1/2} = \mu + \frac{1}{2}\delta$;
(c) $\mu\delta = \frac{1}{2}(E - E^{-1})$;
(d) $E\delta^2 = \Delta^2$;
(e) $\Delta = \mu\delta + \frac{1}{2}\delta^2$;
(f) $\mu^2 = 1 + \frac{\delta^2}{4}$.

9. Employing the operators δ and μ of Exercise 8, show that Stirling's Interpolation Formula may be written in the form

$$y = y_0 + \mu\delta y_0 x + \delta^2 y_0 \frac{x^2}{2!} + \mu\delta^3 y_0 \frac{x(x^2 - 1)}{3!} + \delta^4 y_0 \frac{x^2(x^2 - 1)}{4!}$$

$$+ \mu\delta^5 y_0 \frac{x(x^2 - 1)(x^2 - 2^2)}{5!} + \delta^6 y_0 \frac{x^2(x^2 - 1)(x^2 - 2^2)}{6!} + \cdots.$$

10. Given the points $(0, 1)$, $(1, 3)$, $(2, 9)$, $(3, 6)$, and $(4, 19)$, find $\mu\delta^3 y_2$.

7. FUNCTIONS OF TWO VARIABLES

In many applications of mathematics, we need to consider functions of two or more independent variables. The process of determining an interpolation function for data representing a function of two independent variables is called *double interpolation*. The problem of double interpolation is generally much more difficult than that of *single interpolation*. Interpolation for functions of more than two independent variables represents an extremely difficult problem. In this section, we shall investigate one method of double interpolation.

Consider a function of two independent variables x and y. For convenience, we shall denote the function as z_{xy}; for example, z_{12} shall represent the value of the function for $x = 1$ and $y = 2$. It is evident that x may increase while y remains constant, y may increase while x remains constant, or both may increase simultaneously. If we consider the increments of x and y to be constant and equal to unity, a set of functional values may be represented by Table 2.2.

TABLE 2.2

x \ y	0	1	2	$\cdots$	n
0	z_{00}	z_{01}	z_{02}	$\cdots$	z_{0n}
1	z_{10}	z_{11}	z_{12}	$\cdots$	z_{1n}
2	z_{20}	z_{21}	z_{22}	$\cdots$	z_{2n}
.	.				
.	.				
.	.				
m	z_{m0}	z_{m1}	z_{m2}	$\cdots$	z_{mn}

2.26

To distinguish between increases in x and y, the operator E_x will denote a unit increase in x while y remains constant. The operators E_y, Δ_x, and Δ_y will be defined in a similar fashion. For example,

$$E_x z_{00} = z_{10}, \quad \text{while} \quad E_y z_{00} = z_{01},$$

and

$$\Delta_x z_{00} = z_{10} - z_{00}, \quad \text{while} \quad \Delta_y z_{00} = z_{01} - z_{00}.$$

In addition, note that the order in which the differencing with respect to the two independent variables takes place is immaterial. For example,

$$\begin{aligned}
\Delta_x \Delta_y z_{00} &= \Delta_x(z_{01} - z_{00}) \\
&= \Delta_x z_{01} - \Delta_x z_{00} \\
&= (z_{11} - z_{01}) - (z_{10} - z_{00}) \\
&= z_{11} - z_{01} - z_{10} + z_{00},
\end{aligned}$$

and

$$\Delta_y\Delta_x z_{00} = \Delta_y(z_{10} - z_{00})$$
$$= \Delta_y z_{10} - \Delta_y z_{00}$$
$$= (z_{11} - z_{10}) - (z_{01} - z_{00})$$
$$= z_{11} - z_{10} - z_{01} + z_{00}.$$

Hence,

$$\Delta_x\Delta_y z_{00} = \Delta_y\Delta_x z_{00}.$$

The analogy between the role of the operators Δ_x and Δ_y in the calculus of finite differences and the role of the partial differentiation operators $\dfrac{\partial}{\partial x}$ and $\dfrac{\partial}{\partial y}$ in the calculus of infinitesimals should be immediately evident.

A difference table for a given set of $(m + 1)(n + 1)$ points equally spaced with respect to x and y may be constructed for first-order differences only. Higher-order difference tables are impractical to construct. The scheme in Table 2.3 may be employed to represent the given data and their first differences.

TABLE 2.3

y / x	0		1		2		
0	z_{00}	$(\Delta_y z_{00})$	z_{01}	$(\Delta_y z_{01})$	z_{02}	$(\Delta_y z_{02})$	$\cdots$
	$(\Delta_x z_{00})$		$(\Delta_x z_{01})$		$(\Delta_x z_{02})$		
1	z_{10}	$(\Delta_y z_{10})$	z_{11}	$(\Delta_y z_{11})$	z_{12}	$(\Delta_y z_{12})$	$\cdots$ 2.27
	$(\Delta_x z_{10})$		$(\Delta_x z_{11})$		$(\Delta_x z_{12})$		
2	z_{20}	$(\Delta_y z_{20})$	z_{21}	$(\Delta_y z_{21})$	z_{22}	$(\Delta_y z_{22})$	$\cdots$
	$\cdot$		$\cdot$		$\cdot$		
	$\cdot$		$\cdot$		$\cdot$		
	$\cdot$		$\cdot$		$\cdot$		

EXAMPLE 1.   Construct a two-way table of functional values and first differences for the function $z = x^2 + y - 1$ for $x = 0, 1, 2, 3$ and $y = 0, 1, 2$.

Solution: A table of functional values appears as follows:

y / x	0	1	2
0	-1	0	1
1	0	1	2
2	3	4	5
3	8	9	10

A table of functional values with first differences enclosed in parentheses appears as follows:

$\diagdown$ y x $\diagdown$	0		1		2
0	−1	(1)	0	(1)	1
	(1)		(1)		(1)
1	0	(1)	1	(1)	2
	(3)		(3)		(3)
2	3	(1)	4	(1)	5
	(5)		(5)		(5)
3	8	(1)	9	(1)	10

Note that first differences in every row are constant, while second differences in each column are constant.

The problem of determining an interpolation function $I(x, y)$ for a given set of $(m + 1)(n + 1)$ points, represented by the array of (2.26), under the criterion $I(x_i, y_j) = z_{ij}$ for all i, j may be resolved by considering an extension of the principle by which Newton's Binomial Interpolation Formula was derived. Since

$$z_{mn} = E_x^m E_y^n z_{00} = (1 + \Delta_x)^m (1 + \Delta_y)^n z_{00}, \qquad \textbf{2.28}$$

the corresponding formula for double interpolation becomes

$$I(x, y) = (1 + \Delta_x)^x (1 + \Delta_y)^y z_{00}. \qquad \textbf{2.29}$$

Upon expansion of the binomial factors, equation (2.29) becomes

$$
\begin{aligned}
I(x,y) &= \left[1 + \binom{x}{1}\Delta_x + \binom{x}{2}\Delta_x^2 + \cdots + \binom{x}{m}\Delta_x^m \right] \\
&\quad \times \left[1 + \binom{y}{1}\Delta_y + \binom{y}{2}\Delta_y^2 + \cdots + \binom{y}{n}\Delta_y^n \right] z_{00} \\
&= z_{00} + \left[\binom{x}{1}\Delta_x + \binom{y}{1}\Delta_y \right] z_{00} \\
&\quad + \left[\binom{x}{2}\Delta_x^2 + \binom{x}{1}\binom{y}{1}\Delta_x\Delta_y + \binom{y}{2}\Delta_y^2 \right] z_{00} \qquad \textbf{2.30} \\
&\quad + \left[\binom{x}{3}\Delta_x^3 + \binom{x}{2}\binom{y}{1}\Delta_x^2\Delta_y + \binom{x}{1}\binom{y}{2}\Delta_x\Delta_y^2 + \binom{y}{3}\Delta_y^3 \right] z_{00} + \cdots .
\end{aligned}
$$

It may happen that the rth-order differences with respect to x, where $r < m$, will be constant. In such instances, terms containing higher-order differences with respect to x may be omitted. A similar situation may occur with respect to the y variable.

EXAMPLE 2.   Find an interpolation function $I(x, y)$ such that $I(x_i, y_j) = z_{ij}$, given the following data:

x \ y	0	1	2
0	0	−2	−8
1	3	1	−5
2	6	4	−2

Solution: The table of given functional values with first differences appears as follows:

x \ y	0		1		2
0	0	(−2)	−2	(−6)	−8
	(3)		(3)		(3)
1	3	(−2)	1	(−6)	−5
	(3)		(3)		(3)
2	6	(−2)	4	(−6)	−2

Since first differences with respect to x are constant, higher-order differences for that variable may be neglected in our double interpolation formula. In addition, it should be noted that we need only to consider up to second-order differences with respect to y. Hence,

$$I(x, y) = (1 + \Delta_x)^x(1 + \Delta_y)^y z_{00}$$

$$= \left[1 + \binom{x}{1}\Delta_x\right]\left[1 + \binom{y}{1}\Delta_y + \binom{y}{2}\Delta_y^2\right] z_{00}$$

$$= z_{00} + x\Delta_x z_{00} + y\Delta_y z_{00} + xy\Delta_x\Delta_y z_{00} + \frac{y(y-1)}{2}\Delta_y^2 z_{00}$$

$$+ \frac{xy(y-1)}{2}\Delta_x\Delta_y^2 z_{00}.$$

Now,

$$z_{00} = 0,$$

$$\Delta_x z_{00} = z_{10} - z_{00} = 3 - 0 = 3,$$

$$\Delta_y z_{00} = z_{01} - z_{00} = -2 - 0 = -2,$$

$$\Delta_x\Delta_y z_{00} = z_{11} - z_{01} - z_{10} + z_{00} = 1 - (-2) - 3 + 0 = 0,$$

$$\Delta_y^2 z_{00} = z_{02} - 2z_{01} + z_{00} = -8 - 2(-2) + 0 = -4,$$

$$\Delta_x\Delta_y^2 z_{00} = z_{12} - z_{02} - 2z_{11} + 2z_{01} + z_{10} - z_{00}$$

$$= -5 - (-8) - 2(1) + 2(-2) + 3 - 0$$

$$= 0.$$

Substituting these values in our expression for $I(x, y)$, we have

$$I(x, y) = 0 + 3x - 2y + 0xy - 4 \cdot \frac{y(y - 1)}{2} + 0 \cdot \frac{xy(y - 1)}{2}$$
$$= 3x - 2y - 2y^2 + 2y$$
$$= 3x - 2y^2.$$

EXERCISES

1. Construct a table of functional values and first differences for $z = x^2 - xy + y$ for $x = 0, 1, 2$, and $y = 0, 1, 2, 3$.

2. Construct a table of functional values and first differences for $z = xy + 3x - 2y$ for $x = -1, 0, 1, 2, 3$, and $y = 0, 1, 2, 3$.

3. Find $\Delta_x^3 \Delta_y^2 z_{00}$.

4. Find $z = f(x, y)$, given

$\diagdown$ y x $\diagdown$	0	1	2	3
0	0	0	0	0
1	1	2	3	4
2	2	4	6	8

5. Find $z = f(x, y)$, given

$\diagdown$ y x $\diagdown$	0	1	2	3	4
0	3	2	1	0	-1
1	4	3	2	1	0
2	7	6	5	4	3
3	12	11	10	9	8

6. Given $z_{00} = 5$, $z_{10} = 2$, $z_{01} = 3$, and $z_{11} = 6$, find z_{23}.

7. Find $z = f(x, y)$, given

$\diagdown$ y x $\diagdown$	-1	0	1	2	3	4
-1.5	3	0	3	12	27	48
-1.0	2	0	2	8	18	32
-0.5	1	0	1	4	9	16
0	0	0	0	0	0	0

Hint: Use a transformation of variables.

3

Numerical Differentiation and Integration

I. STIRLING NUMBERS OF THE FIRST KIND

The *factorial polynomial* of degree n

$$P^n(x) = x(x - 1)(x - 2) \cdots (x - n + 1) = x!/(x - n)! \qquad \textbf{3.1}$$

occurs frequently in numerical analysis. Multiplying out the right-hand member of equation (3.1), we have

$$P^n(x) = S_1^n x + S_2^n x^2 + S_3^n x^3 + \cdots + S_n^n x^n = \sum_{i=1}^{n} S_i^n x^i. \qquad \textbf{3.2}$$

The numbers S_i^n are called *Stirling Numbers of the First Kind*. The upper index indicates the degree of the polynomial; the lower index is that of the power of x associated with it.

Now,

$$P^{n+1}(x) = P^n(x)(x - n).$$

Hence,

$$\sum_{i=1}^{n+1} S_i^{n+1} x^i = (x - n) \sum_{i=1}^{n} S_i^n x^i.$$

By equating coefficients of x^i in the above equation, we have the useful relationship

$$S_i^{n+1} = S_{i-1}^n - nS_i^n. \qquad \textbf{3.3}$$

From the definition of a factorial polynomial, note that $S_0^n = 0$ and $S_n^n = 1$. In addition, $S_i^n = 0$ if $i > n$. Now, making use of these particular Stirling numbers and the recurrence relation of (3.3), we are able to construct Table 3.1, a table of Stirling Numbers of the First Kind. Table 3.1 may be used for factorial polynomials of degree eight or lower. The student may, if desired, extend the table for his own use.

TABLE 3.1

STIRLING NUMBERS OF THE FIRST KIND

$n \backslash S_i^n$	S_1^n	S_2^n	S_3^n	S_4^n	S_5^n	S_6^n	S_7^n	S_8^n
1	1							
2	−1	1						
3	2	−3	1					
4	−6	11	−6	1				
5	24	−50	35	−10	1			
6	−120	274	−225	85	−15	1		
7	720	−1764	1624	−735	175	−21	1	
8	−5040	13068	−13132	6769	−1960	322	−28	1

Each entry in Table 3.1 is equal to the entry diagonally above to the left minus the product of the entry directly above and its row number n. For example,

$$S_3^7 = S_2^6 - 6S_3^6;$$

that is,

$$1624 = 274 - 6(-225) = 274 + 1350.$$

An interesting property of the Stirling numbers may be obtained by letting $x = 1$ in equations (3.1) and (3.2). Now, $P^n(1) = 0$ from equation (3.1), and $P^n(1) = S_1^n + S_2^n + \cdots + S_n^n$ from equation (3.2). Hence,

$$\sum_{i=1}^{n} S_i^n = 0. \qquad\qquad \textbf{3.4}$$

That is, the sum of the Stirling Numbers of the First Kind associated with an nth degree factorial polynomial is zero. This property may serve as a check in the construction of Table 3.1 since the entries in any row except the first must add up to zero.

EXAMPLE.   Determine the expanded form of $x(x - 1)(x - 2)(x - 3)$.

Solution: Since $P^4(x) = x(x - 1)(x - 2)(x - 3)$, the coefficients of the ascending powers of x for this fourth degree factorial polynomial are the Stirling numbers S_1^4, S_2^4, S_3^4, and S_4^4, respectively. From Table 3.1, we have $S_1^4 = -6$, $S_2^4 = 11$, $S_3^4 = -6$, and $S_4^4 = 1$. Hence,

$$x(x - 1)(x - 2)(x - 3) = -6x + 11x^2 - 6x^3 + x^4.$$

2. DIFFERENTIATION OF NEWTON'S BINOMIAL INTERPOLATION FORMULA

The problem of obtaining the value of the derivative, at some point, of a function expressed by a set of points is one which should be approached cautiously. It is obvious that we cannot be completely certain of the functional relationship between two variables from a set of empirical values of the variables. Hence, it should be even more obvious that we cannot be certain of the differentiability of the function everywhere. Only if we have some additional information which allows us to assume that the derivative exists at certain points may we reasonably discuss the value of the derivative at these points. Such cases arise often in dealing with physical systems where rates of change are usually well defined.

The process of finding the values of the first derivative of a function at a given point from a table of values of the independent and dependent variables is one of obtaining an interpolation function, differentiating it, and substituting the value of the independent variable for the point in question. This does not present a new problem in methodology. However, if we desire the value of the derivative without obtaining an expression for an interpolation function, then we must approach the problem from another point of view. Essentially, we can obtain for each interpolation formula a new formula which approximates the derivative. We shall illustrate this process for Newton's Binomial Interpolation Formula.

Since Newton's Binomial Interpolation Formula involves the binomial coefficients, we first consider the problem of determining the derivatives of $\binom{x}{k}$. We find that Stirling numbers are quite useful in differentiating the expression $\binom{x}{k}$. Now,

$$\binom{x}{k} = \frac{P^k(x)}{k!}.$$

Therefore,

$$\frac{d\binom{x}{k}}{dx} = \frac{d}{dx}\left[\frac{P^k(x)}{k!}\right]$$

$$= \frac{1}{k!}\frac{d}{dx}[S_1^k x + S_2^k x^2 + S_3^k x^3 + \cdots + S_k^k x^k].$$

Hence,

$$\frac{d\binom{x}{k}}{dx} = \frac{1}{k!}[S_1^k + 2S_2^k x + 3S_3^k x^2 + \cdots + kS_k^k x^{k-1}]. \qquad \textbf{3.5}$$

Upon differentiating Newton's Binomial Interpolation Formula,

$$I(x) = y_0 + \binom{x}{1}\Delta y_0 + \binom{x}{2}\Delta^2 y_0 + \binom{x}{3}\Delta^3 y_0 + \cdots + \binom{x}{n}\Delta^n y_0,$$

we obtain

$$\frac{dI(x)}{dx} = S_1^1 \Delta y_0 + \frac{1}{2!}[S_1^2 + 2S_2^2 x]\Delta^2 y_0 + \frac{1}{3!}[S_1^3 + 2S_2^3 x + 3S_3^3 x^2]\Delta^3 y_0 + \cdots$$

$$+ \frac{1}{n!}[S_1^n + 2S_2^n x + 3S_3^n x^2 + \cdots + nS_n^n x^{n-1}]\Delta^n y_0. \qquad \textbf{3.6}$$

EXAMPLE 1.   Find the derivative of $\binom{x}{4}$.

Solution: Making use of equation (3.5) and Table 3.1, we have

$$\binom{x}{4} = \frac{1}{4!}\,[S_1^4 + 2S_2^4 x + 3S_3^4 x^2 + 4S_4^4 x^3]$$

$$= \frac{1}{4!}\,[-6 + 22x - 18x^2 + 4x^3]$$

$$= \tfrac{1}{6}x^3 - \tfrac{3}{4}x^2 + \tfrac{11}{12}x - \tfrac{1}{4}.$$

EXAMPLE 2.   Find the first derivative of y with respect to x, given the following set of values:

x	0	1	2	3	4	5
y	-1	-1	1	11	35	79

Solution: After constructing the following table of differences, we note that the third differences are constant.

x	y	Δy	$\Delta^2 y$	$\Delta^3 y$
0	-1			
		0		
1	-1		2	
		2		6
2	1		8	
		10		6
3	11		14	
		24		6
4	35		20	
		44		
5	79			

Hence, we need not consider terms of the derivative of our approximation function containing fourth- or higher-order differences. Therefore,

$$\frac{dI(x)}{dx} = S_1^1 \Delta y_0 + \frac{1}{2!}\,[S_1^2 + 2S_2^2 x]\,\Delta^2 y_0 + \frac{1}{3!}\,[S_1^3 + 2S_2^3 x + 3S_3^3 x^2]\,\Delta^3 y_0.$$

Upon substituting the appropriate Stirling Numbers of the First Kind and our leading differences, we obtain

$$\frac{dI(x)}{dx} = \frac{1}{2!}[-1 + 2x](2) + \frac{1}{3!}[2 - 6x + 3x^2](6)$$
$$= -1 + 2x + 2 - 6x + 3x^2$$
$$= 3x^2 - 4x + 1.$$

The correctness of this answer as an approximation derivative may be verified by noting that the approximation polynomial for the given set of values is

$$I(x) = x^3 - 2x^2 + x - 1.$$

EXERCISES

1. Show that:

   (a) $P^n(x) = n! \binom{x}{n}$;

   (b) $P^n(x) = 0$ for $x = 0, 1, 2, \ldots, n - 1$;

   (c) $P^n(x) = \frac{x!}{(x - n)!}$ for $x = n, n + 1, \ldots$.

2. Prove that $P^r(x) \cdot P^n(x - r) = P^{n+r}(x)$.

3. Expand $P^7(x)$.

4. Determine the expanded form of $x(x - 1) \cdots (x - 5)$.

5. Extend Table 3.1 for $n = 9; 10$.

6. Find the derivative of $\binom{x}{6}$.

7. Find $\frac{dy}{dx}$ given the following table of paired values:

x	0	1	2	3	4
y	-2	-1	6	25	62

8. Show that $\dfrac{d}{dx}\binom{x}{n} = \binom{x}{n}\left[\dfrac{1}{x} + \dfrac{1}{x-1} + \dfrac{1}{x-2} + \cdots + \dfrac{1}{x-n+1}\right]$.

9. Show that $\dfrac{d^2}{dx^2}\binom{x}{n} = \dfrac{1}{n}\left[2\dfrac{d\binom{x}{n-1}}{dx} + (x - n + 1)\dfrac{d^2\binom{x}{n-1}}{dx^2}\right]$.

10. A generalization of the results of Exercise 9 for higher-order derivatives is given by

$$\frac{d^k\binom{x}{n}}{dx^k} = \frac{1}{n}\left[k\,\frac{d^{k-1}\binom{x}{n-1}}{dx^{k-1}} + (x - n + 1)\frac{d^k\binom{x}{n-1}}{dx^k} \right].$$

Prove this generalization by mathematical induction.

3. THE RELATION BETWEEN D AND Δ

The difference operator Δ and the differential operator $D \equiv \dfrac{d}{dx}$ are examples of linear operators formally satisfying the laws of algebra, and both may be used symbolically detached from the expressions upon which they operate. It is possible to express the derivative of a function in terms of successive differences, and also to express the difference of a function in terms of its successive derivatives.

Consider the well-known Taylor series expansion

$$f(w) = f(a) + \frac{f'(a)}{1!}(w - a) + \frac{f''(a)}{2!}(w - a)^2 + \cdots + \frac{f^n(a)}{n!}(w - a)^n + \cdots.$$

$$\textbf{3.7}$$

Now, let $w = x + n\Delta x$ and $a = x$. Equation (3.7) becomes

$$f(x + n\,\Delta x) = f(x) + n\,\Delta x f'(x) + \frac{(n\,\Delta x)^2}{2!}f''(x) + \cdots + \frac{(n\,\Delta x)^n}{n!}f^n(x) + \cdots$$

$$= f(x) + n\,\Delta x\, Df(x) + \frac{(n\,\Delta x)^2}{2!}D^2f(x) + \cdots$$

$$+ \frac{(n\,\Delta x)^n}{n!}D^nf(x) + \cdots.$$

By making use of the detached operator convention, we have

$$f(x + n\,\Delta x) = \left[1 + n\,\Delta x\, D + \frac{(n\,\Delta x)^2}{2!}D^2 + \cdots + \frac{(n\,\Delta x)^n}{n!}D^n + \cdots \right]f(x).$$

$$\textbf{3.8}$$

Now, since

$$e^z = 1 + \frac{z}{1!} + \frac{z^2}{2!} + \cdots + \frac{z^n}{n!} + \cdots,$$

the differential operator expression on the right-hand side of equation (3.8) may be written symbolically as $e^{n\Delta x D}$. That is,

$$f(x + n\Delta x) = e^{n\Delta x D}f(x).$$

$$\textbf{3.9}$$

In terms of our difference operators,

$$f(x + n\Delta x) = E^n f(x) \qquad \textbf{3.10}$$

for the interval of differencing Δx. Hence, equation (3.9) becomes

$$E^n f(x) = e^{n\Delta x D} f(x). \qquad \textbf{3.11}$$

Now, consider $\Delta x = 1$ since this is always possible by a transformation of variables. In addition, consider the operators of equation (3.11) detached from $f(x)$. Equation (3.11) may now be written in purely operational form as

$$E^n = e^{nD}. \qquad \textbf{3.12}$$

Taking the natural logarithm of both sides of this equation, we obtain

$$nD = n \ln E;$$

that is,

$$D = \ln E = \ln (1 + \Delta). \qquad \textbf{3.13}$$

Expanding $\ln (1 + \Delta)$ into an infinite series, equation (3.13) becomes

$$D = \Delta - \frac{\Delta^2}{2} + \frac{\Delta^3}{3} - \frac{\Delta^4}{4} + \cdots + (-1)^{n+1}\frac{\Delta^n}{n} + \cdots, \qquad \textbf{3.14}$$

which expresses the differential operator in terms of the successive difference operators. The student should be careful to remember that equation (3.14) should be interpreted to mean

$$Df(x) = \left[\Delta - \frac{\Delta^2}{2} + \frac{\Delta^3}{3} - \frac{\Delta^4}{4} + \cdots + (-1)^{n+1}\frac{\Delta^n}{n} + \cdots\right]f(x);$$

that is,

$$Df(x) = \Delta f(x) - \frac{\Delta^2 f(x)}{2} + \frac{\Delta^3 f(x)}{3} - \frac{\Delta^4 f(x)}{4} + \cdots + (-1)^{n+1}\frac{\Delta^n f(x)}{n} + \cdots. \qquad \textbf{3.15}$$

Since $D^2 = D \cdot D$,

$$D^2 = \left(\Delta - \frac{\Delta^2}{2} + \frac{\Delta^3}{3} - \frac{\Delta^4}{4} + \cdots\right)^2, \qquad \textbf{3.16}$$

or

$$D^2 = \Delta^2 - \Delta^3 + \tfrac{11}{12}\Delta^4 - \tfrac{5}{6}\Delta^5 + \cdots. \qquad \textbf{3.17}$$

Similarly,

$$D^3 = \Delta^3 - \tfrac{3}{2}\Delta^4 + \tfrac{7}{4}\Delta^5 - \cdots. \qquad \textbf{3.18}$$

The process may be extended to obtain any higher-order derivative in terms of successive differences.

To obtain the differences of a function in terms of its successive derivatives, we take the nth root of both sides of equation (3.12). Thus

$$E = e^D. \qquad \textbf{3.19}$$

Replacing E by $1 + \Delta$ and expanding the exponential expression as an infinite series, we obtain

$$\Delta = D + \frac{D^2}{2!} + \frac{D^3}{3!} + \cdots + \frac{D^n}{n!} + \cdots . \qquad \textbf{3.20}$$

By squaring both sides of equation (3.20),

$$\Delta^2 = D^2 + D^3 + \tfrac{7}{12} D^4 + \cdots . \qquad \textbf{3.21}$$

We may extend this process further to obtain higher-order differences in terms of successive derivatives.

EXAMPLE 1.   Find the derivative of $f(x) = x^3 - 2x^2 + 3x - 4$ by obtaining successive differences.

Solution: Since the function is a third degree polynomial, fourth- and higher-order differences vanish. Then,

$$\frac{df(x)}{dx} = \left[\Delta - \frac{\Delta^2}{2} + \frac{\Delta^3}{3} \right] f(x).$$

Now,

$$\begin{aligned}
\Delta(x^3 - 2x^2 + 3x - 4) &= [(x + 1)^3 - 2(x + 1)^2 + 3(x + 1) - 4] \\
&\quad - (x^3 - 2x^2 + 3x - 4) \\
&= 3x^2 - x + 2, \\
\Delta^2(x^3 - 2x^2 + 3x - 4) &= \Delta(3x^2 - x + 2) \\
&= [3(x + 1)^2 - (x + 1) + 2] - (3x^2 - x + 2) \\
&= 6x + 2,
\end{aligned}$$

and

$$\begin{aligned}
\Delta^3(x^3 - 3x^2 + 3x - 4) &= \Delta^2(3x^2 - x + 2) \\
&= \Delta(6x + 2) \\
&= [6(x + 1) + 2] - (6x + 2) \\
&= 6.
\end{aligned}$$

Hence,

$$\begin{aligned}
\Delta f(x) &= 3x^2 - x + 2, \\
\frac{\Delta^2 f(x)}{2} &= 3x + 1,
\end{aligned}$$

and

$$\frac{\Delta^3 f(x)}{3} = 2.$$

Therefore,

$$\begin{aligned}
\frac{df(x)}{dx} &= (3x^2 - x + 2) - (3x + 1) + 2 \\
&= 3x^2 - 4x + 3.
\end{aligned}$$

EXAMPLE 2. Find $\Delta^2 f(3)$ if $f(x) = x^4 - 3x + 1$.

Solution: Since $f(x)$ is a fourth degree polynomial function, fifth- and higher-order derivatives vanish. By equation (3.21),

$$\Delta^2 f(x) = (D^2 + D^3 + \tfrac{7}{12} D^4) f(x).$$

Now,

$$D^2(x^4 - 3x + 1) = 12x^2,$$
$$D^3(x^4 - 3x + 1) = 24x,$$
$$D^4(x^4 - 3x + 1) = 24,$$

and

$$D^2 f(3) = 108, \qquad D^3 f(3) = 72, \qquad D^4 f(3) = 24.$$

Hence,

$$\Delta^2 f(3) = (108) + (72) + \tfrac{7}{12}(24)$$

$$= 194.$$

EXERCISES

1. Find the derivative of $2x^3 - 3x^2 + 4x - 7$ by the difference method.
2. Find the derivative of x^4 by the difference method.
3. Find $\Delta^2 f(x)$ if $f(x) = x^5 - x^3 + 2$.
4. Show that if $\Delta x = h$, equation (3.14) becomes

$$D = \frac{1}{h}\left[\Delta - \frac{\Delta^2}{2} + \frac{\Delta^3}{3} - \frac{\Delta^4}{4} + \cdots + (-1)^{n+1} \frac{\Delta^n}{n} + \cdots \right].$$

5. Determine the first four terms of D^2 and D^3 if $\Delta x = h$.
6. Find Δ in terms of the D operator if $\Delta x = h$.
7. Find Δe^x by making use of the successive derivatives of e^x.

4. THEORY OF NUMERICAL INTEGRATION

In the study of the evaluation of a definite integral, assuming the limits are given, two conditions must hold for an exact evaluation. First, the function to be integrated (or integrand) must be known, and second, the function must be integrable. When these conditions are not satisfied, an alternate course of evaluation is pursued, that of *numerical integration*. Since we may think of integration as the process of finding the area under a curve when the curve represents a function of a single variable, numerical integration is often referred to as *mechanical quadrature*.

Numerical integration is fundamentally the process of computing the value of a definite integral from a set of numerical values of the integrand for given values of the independent variable. This is often necessary in the applied sciences where we may obtain values of the function from observations, but may not be capable or desirous of expressing the data by means of a functional expression. The process involves the substitution of an appropriate expression, generally a polynomial, for the integrand. This polynomial approximates the actual function which the empirical data represent. In many instances, the degree of accuracy desired is tempered by the degree of the polynomial with which the applied mathematician or engineer is willing to work.

Once we have obtained a polynomial which represents the integrand, term by term integration can be accomplished and the definite integral evaluated. However, in many cases, the polynomial function may not be desired and our only interest lies in the value of the definite integral. The intermediate steps of obtaining the polynomial function may be by-passed if quadrature formulas based upon integration of general polynomial approximations can be obtained. We shall now develop these formulas.

5. INTEGRATION OF NEWTON'S BINOMIAL INTERPOLATION FORMULA

Given a set of points (x_0, y_0), (x_1, y_1), $\ldots$, (x_n, y_n) such that the values of x are spaced at equal intervals, that is, $x_1 - x_0 = x_2 - x_1 = \cdots = x_n - x_{n-1} = h$, then Newton's Binomial Interpolation Formula

$$I(x) = y_0 + \frac{\Delta y_0 (x - x_0)}{h} + \frac{\Delta^2 y_0 (x - x_0)(x - x_1)}{2! \, h^2}$$
$$+ \cdots + \frac{\Delta^n y_0 (x - x_0)(x - x_1) \cdots (x - x_{n-1})}{n! \, h^n}$$

represents one form of an approximation polynomial for the integrand. Integrating $I(x)$ over n equal intervals of width h, we have

$$\int_{x_0}^{x_0+nh} I(x) \, dx = \int_{x_0}^{x_0+nh} \left[y_0 + \frac{\Delta y_0 (x - x_0)}{h} + \frac{\Delta^2 y_0 (x - x_0)(x - x_1)}{2! \, h^2} \right.$$
$$+ \frac{\Delta^3 y_0 (x - x_0)(x - x_1)(x - x_2)}{3! \, h^3} + \cdots$$
$$\left. + \frac{\Delta^n y_0 (x - x_0)(x - x_1) \cdots (x - x_{n-1})}{n! \, h^n} \right] dx$$

$$= \left[y_0 x + \frac{\Delta y_0 \left(\frac{x^2}{2} - x_0 x \right)}{h} + \frac{\Delta^2 y_0 \left(\frac{x^3}{3} - \{x_0 + x_1\} \frac{x^2}{2} + x_0 x_1 x \right)}{2! \, h^2} \right.$$
$$+ \frac{\Delta^3 y_0 \left(\frac{x^4}{4} - \{x_0 + x_1 + x_2\} \frac{x^3}{3} + \{x_0 x_1 + x_0 x_2 + x_1 x_2\} \frac{x^2}{2} - x_0 x_1 x_2 x \right)}{3! \, h^3} + \cdots \left. \right]_{x_0}^{x_0+nh} .$$

Hence,

$$\int_{x_0}^{x_0+nh} I(x)\, dx = h\left[ny_0 + \frac{n^2}{2}\Delta y_0 + \left(\frac{n^3}{3} - \frac{n^2}{2}\right)\left(\frac{\Delta^2 y_0}{2!}\right) \right.$$
$$\left. + \left(\frac{n^4}{4} - n^3 + n^2\right)\left(\frac{\Delta^3 y_0}{3!}\right) + \cdots \right].$$

3.22

Equation (3.22) represents the form of the basic quadrature formula over n equal intervals from which we may obtain specific formulas over any given number of points. For example, if we let $n = 1$, thus assuming only two points (x_0, y_0) and (x_1, y_1) given and considering only the first differences, we have

$$\int_{x_0}^{x_0+h} I(x)\, dx = \int_{x_0}^{x_1} I(x)\, dx = h(y_0 + \tfrac{1}{2}\Delta y_0).$$

Substituting $y_1 - y_0$ for Δy_0, we have

$$\int_{x_0}^{x_0+h} I(x)\, dx = \frac{h}{2}(y_1 + y_0),$$

3.23

which is the *trapezoidal rule* for numerical integration. Of course, the rule here applies over one interval, but may be extended over any number of intervals in a manner which we shall illustrate in the next section. The student should interpret the rule geometrically.

6. SIMPSON'S RULE

Letting $n = 2$, equation (3.22) becomes (neglecting all differences above the second-order since we assume only three points given)

$$\int_{x_0}^{x_0+2h} I(x)\, dx = \int_{x_0}^{x_2} I(x)\, dx$$
$$= h\left[2y_0 + 2\Delta y_0 + (\tfrac{8}{3} - 2)\frac{\Delta^2 y}{2} \right]$$
$$= h[2y_0 + 2(y_1 - y_0) + \tfrac{1}{3}(y_2 - 2y_1 + y_0)],$$

and

$$\int_{x_0}^{x_0+2h} I(x)\, dx = \frac{h}{3}(y_2 + 4y_1 + y_0).$$

3.24

This is *Simpson's Rule* for approximate integration.

Simpson's Rule may be extended by considering that if

$$\int_{x_0}^{x_0+2h} I(x)\,dx = \frac{h}{3}(y_2 + 4y_1 + y_0),$$

then

$$\int_{x_0+2h}^{x_0+4h} I(x)\,dx = \frac{h}{3}(y_4 + 4y_3 + y_2),$$

$$\cdots$$

and

$$\int_{x_0+(2n-2)h}^{x_0+2nh} I(x)\,dx = \frac{h}{3}(y_{2n} + 4y_{2n-1} + y_{2n-2}).$$

Summing both sides of these equations, we obtain a more general expression for Simpson's Rule:

$$\int_{x_0}^{x_0+2nh} I(x)\,dx = \frac{h}{3}(y_0 + 4y_1 + 2y_2 + 4y_3 + 2y_4 + \cdots + 4y_{2n-1} + y_{2n}). \quad \textbf{3.25}$$

Simpson's Rule is one of the most useful quadrature formulas in numerical analysis. Note that the interval over which we are integrating must contain an *even number* of subintervals of width h in order for the rule to be applicable, that is, Simpson's Rule may be applied only if an odd number of points are determined.

It is interesting to note that the application of Simpson's Rule yields an exact evaluation of a definite integral of $f(x)$ even if $f(x)$ is a third degree polynomial. Consider the case $f(x) = ax^3 + bx^2 + cx + d$ in which we desire $\int_{-h}^{h} f(x)\,dx$. Now,

$$\int_{-h}^{h} f(x)\,dx = \left[\frac{a}{4}x^4 + \frac{b}{3}x^3 + \frac{c}{2}x^2 + dx\right]_{-h}^{h}$$

$$= \left(\frac{2b}{3}\right)h^3 + 2\,dh.$$

By Simpson's Rule, we have

$$\int_{-h}^{h} f(x)\,dx = \frac{h}{3}[f(-h) + 4f(0) + f(h)]$$

$$= \frac{h}{3}[(-ah^3 + bh^2 - ch + d) + (4d) + (ah^3 + bh^2 + ch + d)]$$

$$= \left(\frac{2b}{3}\right)h^3 + 2\,dh.$$

Since a translation of axis $x' = x + k$ does not affect the area under a given curve over some interval of fixed length, the above proof is general in nature. Hence, Simpson's Rule is exact when $f(x)$ is a polynomial of degree less than four.

EXAMPLE 1.   Find the area under the curve $y = x^3$ from $x = 1$ to $x = 3$ by Simpson's Rule.

Solution: If we choose $h = 1$, equation (3.24) may be applied to this problem, where $y_0 = 1^3$, $y_1 = 2^3$, and $y_2 = 3^3$. Therefore,

$$\int_1^3 I(x)\,dx = \tfrac{1}{3}[27 + 32 + 1]$$
$$= 20.$$

Note that the answer is exact since the function under discussion is a third degree polynomial.

EXAMPLE 2. Determine an approximation to π from the formula

$$\frac{\pi}{4} = \int_0^1 \frac{dx}{(1 + x^2)}$$

with the use of Simpson's Rule.

Solution: Now,

$$\pi = 4\int_0^1 \frac{dx}{(1 + x^2)}.$$

Choosing $h = 0.1$, we need to calculate values of the integrand $\dfrac{1}{(1 + x^2)}$ for $x = 0, 0.1, 0.2, \ldots, 1.0$. These values and the corresponding multipliers for Simpson's Rule appear in Table A.

TABLE A

x	$\dfrac{1}{(1 + x^2)}$	multiplier
0	100/100	1
0.1	100/101	4
0.2	100/104	2
0.3	100/109	4
0.4	100/116	2
0.5	100/125	4
0.6	100/136	2
0.7	100/149	4
0.8	100/164	2
0.9	100/181	4
1.0	100/200	1

Hence, by Simpson's Rule,

$$\pi \approx \frac{(4)(0.1)}{3}[1.000000 + 3.960396 + 1.923077 + 3.669725 + 1.724138$$
$$+ 3.200000 + 1.470588 + 2.684564$$
$$+ 1.219512 + 2.209945 + 0.500000]$$
$$\approx 3.141593.$$

The result is correct to six decimal places.

7. OTHER QUADRATURE FORMULAS

The numerical integration formulas developed in the previous sections could have been derived more easily in a separate manner. However, their derivations from the same formula, Newton's Binomial Interpolation Formula, illustrate the relation that exists among them. In addition, we have illustrated the usefulness of this one particular formula in developing additional quadrature formulas by merely increasing the value of n. Each increase of n by unity adds one term to Newton's Binomial Interpolation Formula and assumes the curve to pass through an additional point of data. Had we included one additional term in our work in calculating Simpson's Rule, thereby assuming the approximation curve to pass through four equidistant points with respect to the independent variable, another quadrature formula which is known as the *three-eighths rule* would have been obtained. Letting $n = 3$, we have

$$\int_{x_0}^{x_0+3h} I(x)\, dx = h\left[3y_0 + \tfrac{9}{2}(y_1 - y_0) + \frac{(9 - \tfrac{9}{2})(y_2 - 2y_1 + y_0)}{2!} \right.$$
$$\left. + \frac{(\tfrac{81}{4} - 27 + 9)(y_3 - 3y_2 + 3y_1 - y_0)}{3!}\right];$$

that is,

$$\int_{x_0}^{x_0+3h} I(x)\, dx = \frac{3h}{8}(y_0 + 3y_1 + 3y_2 + y_3). \qquad \textbf{3.26}$$

Extending equation (3.26) by the same principle applied to Simpson's Rule, we obtain the more general form

$$\int_{x_0}^{x_0+3nh} I(x)\, dx = \frac{3h}{8}(y_0 + 3y_1 + 3y_2 + 2y_3 + 3y_4 + 3y_5 \qquad \textbf{3.27}$$
$$+ 2y_6 + \cdots + 3y_{3n-1} + y_{3n}).$$

If we let $n = 6$ after integrating Newton's Binomial Interpolation Formula, we obtain a formula which yields an exact evaluation of a definite integral of $f(x)$ if $f(x)$ is a sixth degree polynomial. The formula is rather complicated. However, by a substitution of $\dfrac{42}{140}\Delta^6 y_0$ for $\dfrac{41}{140}\Delta^6 y_0$, the formula may be written in a simplified form known as *Weddle's Rule*. That is,

$$\int_{x_0}^{x_0+6h} I(x)\, dx = \frac{3h}{10}(y_0 + 5y_1 + y_2 + 6y_3 + y_4 + 5y_5 + y_6), \qquad \textbf{3.28}$$

or, more generally,

$$\int_{x_0}^{x_0+6nh} I(x)\, dx = \frac{3h}{10}\sum_{i=0}^{6n} k_i y_i, \qquad \textbf{3.29}$$

where $k_i = 1, 5, 1, 6, 1, 5, 2, 5, 1, 6, 1, 5, 2, \ldots, 5, 1$ as $i = 0, 1, 2, 3, 4, 5, 6, 7, 8, 9, 10, 11, 12, \ldots, 6n - 1, 6n$, respectively. The use of Weddle's Rule in evaluating a definite integral of $f(x)$ where $f(x)$ is a sixth degree polynomial involves an error of $\dfrac{h}{140} \Delta^6 y_0$.

In general, we may say that Weddle's Rule is more accurate than quadrature formulas involving interpolation polynomials of a lower degree. However, a decided disadvantage in the use of this rule is that the number of subintervals involved in its use must be a multiple of six.

The usefulness of Newton's Binomial Interpolation Formula in numerical integration should be evident. It serves as a general expression for the derivation of many mechanical quadrature formulas. Mention should also be made that other quadrature formulas may be developed for other integral values of n. Additional quadrature formulas may be obtained by considering other forms of the interpolation function, such as those given by Stirling's and Bessel's Interpolation Formulas.

EXAMPLE.   Find an approximation to ln 2 by means of Weddle's Rule.

Solution: We must first express ln 2 as a definite integral whose value will be approximated by the use of Weddle's Rule. Since

$$\ln x = \int_1^x \frac{dz}{z},$$

we have

$$\ln 2 = \int_1^2 \frac{dz}{z}.$$

Now, h must be chosen such that the interval from 1 to 2 will be subdivided into $6n$ subintervals. We shall simply choose $h = \dfrac{1}{6}$. Values for the integrand $\dfrac{1}{z}$ at $z = 1, \dfrac{7}{6}, \dfrac{8}{6}, \ldots, 2$ with the corresponding multipliers for Weddle's Rule appear in Table B.

TABLE B

z	$\dfrac{1}{z}$	multiplier
1	1	1
7/6	6/7	5
8/6	6/8	1
9/6	6/9	6
10/6	6/10	1
11/6	6/11	5
2	1/2	1

Therefore, by equation (3.28),

$$\ln 2 \approx \frac{3(\frac{1}{6})}{10} (1 + \tfrac{30}{7} + \tfrac{3}{4} + 4 + \tfrac{3}{5} + \tfrac{30}{11} + \tfrac{1}{2})$$

$$\approx \tfrac{1}{20}(1.000000 + 4.285714 + 0.750000 + 4.000000$$

$$+ 0.600000 + 2.727273 + 0.500000)$$

$$\approx \tfrac{1}{20}(13.862987)$$

$$\approx 0.693149.$$

The correct value of ln 2 to six decimal places is 0.693147.

8. COMMENTS

In the quadrature formulas we have discussed, the values of the independent variable were equally spaced. Mention should be made of the problem of evaluating a definite integral by means of sets of values unequally spaced with respect to the independent variable. This problem is extremely important with regard to the problem of collecting empirical data. The question as to whether or not data should be collected equally spaced was answered by Gauss. If we can choose our points for a numerical integration problem, they should not be chosen equally spaced with respect to the independent variable. Very definite rules for the choice are established by Gauss' method. Theoretically, Gauss' method is extremely accurate. However, the method is also quite laborious unless proper computing facilities are available.

We have not discussed in any detail the problem of the errors involved in the application of the various numerical integration formulas. Methods are available for the determination of such errors when the function being integrated numerically is known. These methods are beyond the scope of this text. In the case where the function is not known, but is expressed by means of a set of points (x_0, y_0), (x_1, y_1), ..., we can, of course, make only weak statements about the error involved in applying a numerical integration formula. Very often a plot of the given points or the given function may indicate an appropriate choice of the degree of the interpolation polynomial to be integrated.

EXERCISES

1. Show that the trapezoidal rule over n intervals is of the form

$$\int_{x_0}^{x_0+nh} I(x)\, dx = h\left[\frac{y_0}{2} + y_1 + y_2 + \cdots + y_{n-1} + \frac{y_n}{2}\right].$$

2. Find $\int_0^1 \sin x\, dx$ by the extended trapezoidal rule and by Simpson's Rule, using $h = 0.1$. Compare the relative errors of each result.

3. Find ln 2 by means of the extended trapezoidal rule and by Simpson's Rule, using $h = 0.1$. Calculate and compare the relative errors obtained by each method.

4. Calculate $\int_0^6 x^6 \, dx$ by Weddle's Rule and by the three-eighths rule. Use $h = 1$. Compare the results.

5. Given the following set of values

x	0	1	2	3	4	5	6	7	8	9	10	11	12
y	5	-2	-17	-34	-47	-50	-37	-2	61	158	295	478	713

determine $\int_0^6 y \, dx, \int_6^{12} y \, dx$, and $\int_0^{12} y \, dx$ by the trapezoidal rule, Simpson's Rule, the three-eighths rule, and Weddle's Rule. Use $h = 1$.

6. Show that

$$\int_{x_0}^{x_4} y \, dx = \frac{4h}{9} (y_0 + 2y_1 + 3y_2 + 2y_3 + y_4)$$

is exact if y is any polynomial of the third degree.

7. Obtain a quadrature formula using a fourth degree interpolation polynomial. Verify its exactness by finding $\int_2^6 x^4 \, dx$, using $h = 1$.

8. Obtain Weddle's Rule by combining a seven-ordinate Simpson's formula with a seven-ordinate three-eighths formula in the ratio 9: -4 and averaging.

4

Summation of Series

I. FUNDAMENTAL THEORY

Given the first several terms of a sequence, the problem of determining succeeding terms by the methods of finite differences and the assumptions pertaining to these methods has already been examined. Consider the problem of determining a general formula for the sum of the first n terms of a given sequence; that is, the problem of the summation of a series.

Let $f(x)$ be a function whose first difference is $g(x)$. That is,

$$\Delta f(x) = g(x).$$

Consider the interval of differencing to be unity. Then, by definition,

$$\Delta f(\alpha) = f(\alpha + 1) - f(\alpha) = g(\alpha),$$
$$\Delta f(\alpha + 1) = f(\alpha + 2) - f(\alpha + 1) = g(\alpha + 1), \qquad \textbf{4.1}$$
$$\dots$$
$$\Delta f[\alpha + (n - 1)] = f[\alpha + n] - f[\alpha + (n - 1)] = g[\alpha + (n - 1)].$$

Upon summing the equations of (4.1), we obtain

$$f(\alpha + n) - f(\alpha) = \sum_{x=0}^{n-1} g(\alpha + x). \qquad \textbf{4.2}$$

Letting $\alpha = 1$, equation (4.2) becomes

$$[f(x)]_1^{n+1} = \sum_{x=1}^{n} g(x), \qquad \textbf{4.3}$$

where

$$[f(x)]_1^{n+1} = f(n + 1) - f(1). \qquad \textbf{4.4}$$

Equation (4.3) means that we can sum a series whose nth term is $g(x)$ if we recognize $g(x)$ as the first difference of some function $f(x)$. To sum the first n terms of the series generated by $g(x)$, compute the difference of $f(x)$ evaluated at $n + 1$ and 1.

2. POLYNOMIAL FORMS OF g(x)

Factorial polynomials are extremely useful in handling the summation problem. Consider the first differences of $P^n(x)$. Now,

$$\Delta P^n(x) = P^n(x+1) - P^n(x)$$
$$= (x+1)(x)(x-1)\cdots(x-n+2) - (x)(x-1)\cdots(x-n+2)$$
$$(x-n+1)$$
$$= x(x-1)\cdots(x-n+2)[(x+1)-(x-n+1)]$$
$$= nx(x-1)\cdots(x-n+2)$$
$$= nP^{n-1}(x).$$

Hence,

$$P^{n-1}(x) = \frac{1}{n}\Delta P^n(x). \qquad \textbf{4.5}$$

Therefore, any series whose generating function is a factorial polynomial may be summed since every factorial polynomial is the first difference of another factorial polynomial one degree higher.

It can be shown that every polynomial of degree n may be expressed as the sum of not more than $n+1$ factorial polynomials if we define a factorial polynomial of degree zero as unity; that is, $P^0(x) = 1$. (See Section 4.3.) Consider any polynomial function

$$p(x) = a_n x^n + a_{n-1}x^{n-1} + \cdots + a_1 x + a_0.$$

Now,

$$p(x) = a_n P^n(x) + R_1,$$

where R_1 is a polynomial function of the $(n-1)$th degree or lower. That is,

$$R_1 = b_{n-1}x^{n-1} + b_{n-2}x^{n-2} + \cdots + b_1 x + b_0.$$

In similar fashion to the above,

$$R_1 = b_{n-1}P^{n-1}(x) + R_2,$$

where

$$R_2 = c_{n-2}x^{n-2} + c_{n-3}x^{n-3} + \cdots + c_1 x + c_0.$$

Eventually we obtain, after a finite number of steps, an R_i equal to zero.

To illustrate the process, let

$$p(x) = 2x^3 - 3x^2 + 5x - 10.$$

With the help of a table of Stirling Numbers of the First Kind, the following schematic may be constructed:

$$p(x) = 2P^3(x) + 3x^2 + x - 10,$$
$$3x^2 + x - 10 = 3P^2(x) + 4x - 10,$$
$$4x - 10 = 4P^1(x) - 10,$$
$$-10 = -10P^0(x).$$

Hence,

$$p(x) = 2P^3(x) + 3P^2(x) + 4P^1(x) - 10P^0(x).$$

An alternate method of expressing polynomials in terms of factorial polynomials makes use of synthetic division. Consider a general nth degree polynomial expressed in factorial form

$$p(x) = k_n P^n(x) + k_{n-1} P^{n-1}(x) + \cdots + k_2 P^2(x) + k_1 P^1(x) + k_0 P^0(x). \quad \textbf{4.6}$$

Repeated divisions of $p(x)$ by the linear factors $x, x - 1, x - 2, \ldots$ produce remainders of $k_0, k_1, k_2, \ldots$, respectively. Hence, if we divide synthetically by $0, 1, 2, \ldots, n$, the remainders taken in reverse order yield the coefficients of our factorial polynomials.

Consider the previous example in which $p(x) = 2x^3 - 3x^2 + 5x - 10$. Dividing synthetically by 0, 1, 2, and 3 yields the following pattern:

1	2	−3	5	−10
	0	2	−1	
2	2	−1	4	
	0	4		
3	2	3		
	0			
	2			

Hence, $p(x) = 2P^3(x) + 3P^2(x) + 4P^1(x) - 10P^0(x)$.

Since every polynomial may be expressed in terms of factorial polynomials which may in turn be considered as first differences of related known factorial polynomials, we are able to evaluate the sum of any series whose generating function is a polynomial, or which may be assumed to be a polynomial.

EXAMPLE 1.   Find the sum of the series

$$1^2 + 2^2 + 3^2 + \cdots + n^2.$$

Solution: The generating function is x^2. Since

$$x^2 = P^2(x) + P^1(x),$$

$$\sum_{x=1}^{n} x^2 = \sum_{x=1}^{n} [P^2(x) + P^1(x)].$$

Now, according to equation (4.5),

$$\sum_{x=1}^{n} [P^2(x) + P^1(x)] = [\tfrac{1}{3}P^3(x) + \tfrac{1}{2}P^2(x)]_1^{n+1}$$

$$= \tfrac{1}{3}P^3(n + 1) + \tfrac{1}{2}P^2(n + 1)$$

$$= \frac{(n + 1)(n)(n - 1)}{3} + \frac{(n + 1)(n)}{2}$$

$$= \frac{n(n + 1)(2n + 1)}{6}.$$

Hence,

$$\sum_{x=1}^{n} x^2 = \frac{n(n + 1)(2n + 1)}{6}.$$

We may verify our results by taking $n = 5$:

$$1^2 + 2^2 + 3^2 + 4^2 + 5^2 = 55$$

and

$$\frac{5(5 + 1)(10 + 1)}{6} = 55.$$

EXAMPLE 2.   Find the sum of the first n terms of the series whose xth term is $x^3 + 5x$.

Solution: Now, $x^3 + 5x = P^3(x) + 3P^2(x) + 6P^1(x)$. Hence,

$$\sum_{x=1}^{n}(x^3 + 5x) = [\tfrac{1}{4}P^4(x) + P^3(x) + 3P^2(x)]_1^{n+1}$$

$$= \frac{(n + 1)(n)(n - 1)(n - 2)}{4} + (n + 1)(n)(n - 1) + 3(n + 1)(n)$$

$$= \tfrac{1}{4}n(n + 1)(n^2 + n + 10).$$

We now discuss a most important and useful application of the polynomial form. A polynomial form may be obtained for the generating function of a series, whose first several terms are given, by the application of Newton's Binomial Interpolation Formula. Again, the student should be fully aware of the assumptions under which such application is being made. In such cases, every term of the interpolation formula involves a factor of the form $\binom{x}{n}$. It would be possible to sum the series immediately, without making direct use of factorial polynomials, if we could obtain a functional expression whose first differences are of the form $\binom{x}{n}$. Such a function is $\binom{x}{n + 1}$.

Theorem.

$$\Delta\binom{x}{n + 1} = \binom{x}{n}.$$ **4.7**

Proof:

$$\Delta\binom{x}{n + 1} = \frac{(x + 1)!}{(n + 1)! \, (x - n)!} - \frac{x!}{(n + 1)! \, (x - n - 1)!}$$

$$= \frac{(x + 1)! - (x - n)x!}{(n + 1)! \, (x - n)!}$$

$$= \frac{(n + 1)x!}{(n + 1)! \, (x - n)!}$$

$$= \frac{x!}{n! \, (x - n)!}.$$

Hence,

$$\Delta\binom{x}{n + 1} = \binom{x}{n}.$$

EXAMPLE 3.   Sum the series $1 + 8 + 27 + 64 + 125 + \cdots$ to n terms.

Solution: We shall assume the generating function $g(x)$ to be a polynomial. We obtain Difference Table A.

Difference Table A

x	$g(x)$	Δ	Δ^2	Δ^3
0	1			
		7		
1	8		12	
		19		6
2	27		18	
		37		6
3	64		24	
		61		
4	125			

Third differences are constant. Employing Newton's Binomial Interpolation Formula, we obtain

$$g(x) = 1 + 7\binom{x}{1} + 12\binom{x}{2} + 6\binom{x}{3}.$$

In order to obtain a sum for the first n terms, we sum $g(x)$ over x from 0 to $n - 1$. Hence,

$$\sum_{x=0}^{n-1} g(x) = [f(x)]_0^n$$

$$= \left[\binom{x}{1} + 7\binom{x}{2} + 12\binom{x}{3} + 6\binom{x}{4} \right]_0^n$$

$$= \binom{n}{1} + 7\binom{n}{2} + 12\binom{n}{3} + 6\binom{n}{4}$$

$$= \frac{n^2(n + 1)^2}{4}.$$

The results will be recognized as $\sum_{x=1}^{n} x^3$.

EXERCISES

1. Express the following polynomials in factorial form:
   (a) $x^2 + 2x - 4$;   (b) $2x^3 + x^2 - 7x - 4$;   (c) $x^3 - x + 12$;
   (d) $x^5 - 3x^3 + x$;   (e) x^4.
2. Sum the following series:
   (a) $1 + 2 + 3 + \cdots + n$;
   (b) $3 + 17 + 33 + 51 + 71 + \cdots$ to n terms;
   (c) $2 + 12 + 36 + 80 + 150 + 252 + \cdots$ to n terms;

    (d) $-1 + 6 + 25 + 62 + 123 + \cdots$ to 15 terms;
    (e) $1 + 1 + 3 + 7 + 13 + \cdots$ to n terms;
    (f) $0 + 0 + 0 + 1 + 1 + 3 + 7 + 13 + \cdots$ to n terms.

3. Sum the first n terms of the series whose generating functions are:
    (a) $x(x - 1)(x - 2)$;
    (b) $x^3 + 3x$;
    (c) x^4;
    (d) $(x + 3)(x + 4)(x + 5)$.

4. Prove that $\Delta P^n(x) = nhP^{n-1}(x)$, where h is the interval of differencing. Consider $P^n(x) = x(x - h)(x - 2h) \cdots (x - (n - 1)h)$.

5. Find an expression for $\Delta^k P^n(x)$, where the interval of differencing is unity.

6. Find an expression for $\Delta^k \binom{x}{n}$, where the interval of differencing is unity.

7. Show that $\displaystyle\sum_{r=0}^{k} P^n(x + r) = \frac{1}{n + 1} [P^{n+1}(x + k + 1) - P^{n+1}(x)]$.

8. Find $\Sigma\, I(x)$ where $I(x)$ is Gauss' Forward Interpolation Formula.

9. Derive equation (4.3) by making use of the operator E.
$$\left(Hint:\ 1 + E + E^2 + \cdots + E^{n-1} = \frac{E^n - 1}{E - 1} \cdot \right)$$

10. If $\Delta f(x) = g(x)$, we shall write $f(x) = \dfrac{1}{\Delta} g(x)$ or $f(x) = \Delta^{-1}g(x)$. The operation Δ^{-1} defines the inverse operation to differencing, *finite integration.* Prove $\Delta\Sigma = 1$; hence, $\Sigma = \Delta^{-1}$. Show that, generally, $\Delta\Sigma \neq \Sigma\,\Delta$. (*Hint:* Given $g(x)$, $f(x)$ is not uniquely determined.)

11. Find:
    (a) $\Delta^{-1}P^n(x)$;
    (b) $\Delta^{-1}\binom{x}{n}$;
    (c) $\Delta^{-1}(x^3 + 2x^2 - 7x + 4)$.

3. OTHER FORMS OF g(x)

Other functional forms beside that of the polynomial often appear as the generating function of a series. Only a limited number of these functional forms may be expressed as the first differences of other simple elementary functions. We shall now examine two of these forms.

Consider the first differences of the exponential function a^x. Now,

$$\Delta a^x = a^{x+1} - a^x$$
$$= a^x \cdot a - a^x$$
$$= a^x(a - 1).$$

Hence,

$$\Delta \frac{a^x}{a - 1} = a^x. \qquad\qquad \textbf{4.8}$$

Therefore, any series whose generating function is of the form ka^x may be summed.

EXAMPLE 1.   Sum the series $6 + 18 + 54 + 162 + 486 + \cdots$ to n terms.

Solution: By examination, we determine the generating function of the series to be of the form $2 \cdot 3^x$. Making use of equation (4.8), we have

$$2 \cdot \Delta \frac{3^x}{3 - 1} = 2 \cdot 3^x,$$

or

$$\Delta 3^x = 2 \cdot 3^x.$$

Hence,

$$\sum_{x=1}^{n} 2 \cdot 3^x = [3^x]_1^{n+1}$$
$$= 3^{n+1} - 3$$
$$= 3(3^n - 1).$$

EXAMPLE 2.   Derive the formula for the sum of n terms of any geometric series, $k + kr + kr^2 + \cdots + kr^{n-1}$.

Solution: Now,

$$k + kr + kr^2 + \cdots + kr^{n-1} = \sum_{x=0}^{n-1} kr^x,$$

and

$$kr^x = k \, \Delta \frac{r^x}{r - 1}.$$

Therefore,

$$\sum_{x=0}^{n-1} kr^x = k \sum_{x=0}^{n-1} \left[\Delta \frac{r^x}{r - 1} \right]$$
$$= k \left[\frac{r^x}{r - 1} \right]_0^n.$$

Hence,

$$\sum_{x=0}^{n-1} kr^x = \frac{k(r^n - 1)}{r - 1}.$$

We have already defined the factorial polynomial $P^n(x)$ for positive integral values of n. It is desirable to consider a definition for $P^n(x)$ when n is zero or a negative integer. The equation

$$P^n(x) = (x - n + 1)P^{n-1}(x) \qquad \qquad \textbf{4.9}$$

is valid for any positive integer n. We shall now accept equation (4.9) as a revised definition of $P^n(x)$ for *any* integer n.

Letting $n = 1$, we have

$$P(x) = xP^0(x).$$

Hence,

$$P^0(x) = 1. \qquad \textbf{4.10}$$

Letting $n = 0$,

$$P^0(x) = (x + 1)P^{-1}(x),$$

whereby

$$P^{-1}(x) = \frac{1}{(x + 1)}.$$

By means of mathematical induction, we may show, in general, that

$$P^{-n}(x) = \frac{1}{(x + 1)(x + 2) \cdots (x + n)} = \frac{1}{P^n(x + n)} \qquad \textbf{4.11}$$

where n is a positive integer. Now,

$$\Delta P^{-n}(x) = \frac{1}{P^n(x + n + 1)} - \frac{1}{P^n(x + n)}$$

$$= \frac{1}{(x + n + 1)(x + n) \cdots (x + 2)} - \frac{1}{(x + n)(x + n - 1) \cdots (x + 1)}$$

$$= \frac{(x + 1) - (x + n + 1)}{(x + n + 1)(x + n) \cdots (x + 1)}$$

$$= \frac{-n}{P^{n+1}(x + n + 1)}$$

$$= -nP^{-n-1}(x),$$

and

$$P^{-n-1}(x) = -\frac{1}{n}\Delta P^{-n}(x). \qquad \textbf{4.12}$$

Equation (4.12) expresses the same relationship as equation (4.5). Hence, we have shown that equation (4.5) is valid for any positive or negative integer n. Note that equation (4.5) is not valid when n is zero.

EXAMPLE 3.   Find the sum of the series

$$\frac{1}{2 \cdot 3} + \frac{1}{3 \cdot 4} + \cdots + \frac{1}{(n + 1)(n + 2)}.$$

Solution: The generating function of the series may be considered to be

$$g(x) = \frac{1}{(x + 1)(x + 2)},$$

or

$$g(x) = P^{-2}(x).$$

Then we desire to find $\sum_{x=1}^{n} g(x)$.

According to equation (4.12),

$$P^{-2}(x) = -\Delta P^{-1}(x).$$

Hence,

$$\sum_{x=1}^{n} g(x) = -\sum_{x=1}^{n} \Delta P^{-1}(x)$$

$$= -[P^{-1}(x)]_1^{n+1}$$

$$= -\left[\frac{1}{P(x+1)}\right]_1^{n+1}$$

$$= -\left[\frac{1}{x+1}\right]_1^{n+1}$$

$$= \frac{n}{2(n+2)}.$$

EXERCISES

In Exercises 1 through 4, sum the given series:

1. $\dfrac{1}{1 \cdot 2 \cdot 3} + \dfrac{1}{2 \cdot 3 \cdot 4} + \dfrac{1}{3 \cdot 4 \cdot 5} + \cdots$ to n terms.

2. $\dfrac{1}{1 \cdot 3} + \dfrac{1}{3 \cdot 5} + \dfrac{1}{5 \cdot 7} + \cdots$ to n terms.

3. $5 + 10 + 17 + 28 + 47 + 82 + \cdots$ to n terms.

4. $1 + 0 + 1 + 8 + 29 + 80 + 193 + \cdots$ to 15 terms.

5. Find $\displaystyle\sum_{x=a}^{b} \dfrac{1}{x(x-1)(x-2)(x-3)}$.

6. Find $\displaystyle\sum_{x=1}^{n} \dfrac{1}{(2x-3)(2x-5)}$.

7. Find $\Delta^{-1} e^x$.

8. Prove equation (4.11) by mathematical induction.

4. SUMMATION BY PARTS

Consider the problem of obtaining the first differences of the product of two functions of x. Let $u(x)$ and $v(x)$ be any two functions of x. Now,

$$\Delta[u(x)v(x)] = u(x+1)v(x+1) - u(x)v(x)$$
$$= v(x+1)[u(x+1) - u(x)] + u(x)[v(x+1) - v(x)]$$
$$= v(x+1)\Delta u(x) + u(x)\Delta v(x).$$

Writing this useful and interesting relationship in another form, we have

$$u(x)\Delta v(x) = \Delta[u(x)v(x)] - v(x+1)\Delta u(x). \qquad \textbf{4.13}$$

Hence,

$$\sum_{x=1}^{n} u(x)\Delta v(x) = [u(x)v(x)]_1^{n+1} - \sum_{x=1}^{n} v(x+1)\Delta u(x). \qquad \textbf{4.14}$$

Equation (4.14) allows us to sum series whose generating function can be written as the product of two functions $u(x)$ and $\Delta v(x)$, provided we can find $v(x)$ and evaluate $\Sigma\, v(x+1)\Delta u(x)$. This method of summing series is extremely useful for complicated forms of the generating function. Considerable skill and ingenuity on the part of the student is necessary in defining the factors of $g(x)$ as $u(x)$ and $\Delta v(x)$. Note that $\Delta v(x)$ should be chosen such that $v(x)$ is easily determined.

EXAMPLE 1. Find the sum of the series

$$3 + 2\cdot 3^2 + 3\cdot 3^3 + \cdots + n\cdot 3^n.$$

Solution: The generating function is of the form $x\cdot 3^x$. If we choose $u(x) = x$ and $\Delta v(x) = 3^x$, then $\Delta u(x) = 1$, $v(x) = \dfrac{3^x}{2}$, and $v(x+1) = \dfrac{3\cdot 3^x}{2}$. Applying equation (4.14), we have

$$\sum_{x=1}^{n} x\cdot 3^x = \left[\frac{x\cdot 3^x}{2}\right]_1^{n+1} - \frac{3}{2}\sum_{x=1}^{n} 3^x$$

$$= \left[\frac{x\cdot 3^x}{2}\right]_1^{n+1} - \frac{3}{2}\cdot\frac{1}{2}[3^x]_1^{n+1}$$

$$= \tfrac{3}{4}[(2n-1)3^n + 1].$$

EXAMPLE 2. Find the sum of the series

$$1\cdot\tfrac{2}{2} + 2\cdot\tfrac{3}{4} + 3\cdot\tfrac{4}{8} + \cdots \text{ to } n \text{ terms}.$$

Solution: By inspection, the generating function is assumed to be of the form $\dfrac{x(x+1)}{2^x}$. If we choose $u(x) = x(x+1)$ and $\Delta v(x) = 2^{-x}$, then $\Delta u(x) = 2(x+1)$, $v(x) = -2^{1-x}$, and $v(x+1) = -2^{-x}$. Summing by parts,

$$\sum_{x=1}^{n} \frac{x(x+1)}{2^x} = \left[\frac{-x(x+1)}{2^{x-1}}\right]_1^{n+1} + 2\sum_{x=1}^{n} \frac{x+1}{2^x}.$$

Applying the method of summation by parts once again to the expression $\Sigma\,\dfrac{x+1}{2^x}$, we let $u(x) = x + 1$ and $\Delta v(x) = 2^{-x}$. Then $\Delta u(x) = 1$, $v(x) = -2^{1-x}$, $v(x+1) = -2^{-x}$, and

$$\sum_{x=1}^{n} \frac{x+1}{2^x} = \left[\frac{-(x+1)}{2^{x-1}}\right]_1^{n+1} + \sum_{x=1}^{n} 2^{-x}$$

$$= \left[\frac{-(x+1)}{2^{x-1}}\right]_1^{n+1} + \left[\frac{-1}{2^{x-1}}\right]_1^{n+1}.$$

Therefore,

$$\sum_{x=1}^{n} \frac{x(x+1)}{2^x} = \left[\frac{-x(x+1)}{2^{x-1}}\right]_1^{n+1} + 2\left[\frac{-(x+1)}{2^{x-1}}\right]_1^{n+1} + 2\left[\frac{-1}{2^{x-1}}\right]_1^{n+1}$$

$$= \left[\frac{-x(x+1) - 2(x+1) - 2}{2^{x-1}}\right]_1^{n+1}$$

$$= 8 - \frac{n^2 + 5n + 8}{2^n}.$$

EXERCISES

1. Find $\sum_{x=1}^{n} 3^x P^2(x)$.

2. Find the sum of the first n terms of the series whose generating function is

$$\frac{x+3}{x(x+1)(x+2)}.$$

3. Find the sum of the series

$$\frac{1}{1} + \frac{1}{1+2} + \frac{1}{1+2+3} + \cdots + \frac{1}{1+2+3+\cdots+n}.$$

4. Find $\sum_{x=1}^{n} \frac{2x+3}{3^x x(x+1)}$.

5. Find $\Delta^{-1}(x^2 2^x)$.

6. Evaluate $\sum_{x=1}^{n} x(x!)$.

7. Sum the infinite series

$$\frac{3}{2 \cdot 5 \cdot 8} + \frac{5}{5 \cdot 8 \cdot 11} + \frac{7}{8 \cdot 11 \cdot 14} + \cdots.$$

8. Evaluate $\sum_{x=1}^{n} \frac{x2^x}{(x+1)(x+2)}$.

9. Prove by mathematical induction that

$$\Delta^n[u(x)v(x)] = u(x)\, \Delta^n v(x) + \binom{n}{1} \Delta\, u(x)\, \Delta^{n-1} v(x+1)$$

$$+ \binom{n}{2} \Delta^2 u(x)\, \Delta^{n-2} v(x+2) + \cdots + \Delta^n u(x)v(x+n).$$

10. Evaluate

$$\frac{1}{x+1} - \frac{n}{(x+1)(x+2)} + \frac{n(n-1)}{(x+1)(x+2)(x+3)} - \cdots$$

$$+ \frac{(-1)^n n!}{(x+1)(x+2)\cdots(x+n+1)}.$$

5

Matrices and Systems
of Linear Equations

I. INTRODUCTION

A set of equations of the form:

$$\begin{cases} a_{11}x_1 + a_{12}x_2 + \cdots + a_{1n}x_n = c_1, \\ a_{21}x_1 + a_{22}x_2 + \cdots + a_{2n}x_n = c_2, \\ \cdots \\ a_{n1}x_1 + a_{n2}x_2 + \cdots + a_{nn}x_n = c_n, \end{cases} \qquad \textbf{5.1}$$

is called a *system of linear equations* in $x_1, x_2, \ldots, x_n$. The n equations represent conditions imposed simultaneously on the variables. The solution set of such a linear system, if it exists, consists of the set of assignable values for $x_1, x_2, \ldots, x_n$ which satisfy the n equations simultaneously.

The solution of systems of linear equations is one of the most important problems which has confronted mathematicians for many centuries. Originally, such problems arose in handling data obtained from astronomical observations. Today, many industrial and engineering problems are resolved by the solution of such linear systems. The main objective of this chapter will be to describe several methods of solution. Since the algebra of matrices facilitates the study of linear systems, we shall devote a major portion of our effort to the theory of matrices.

However, before proceeding to the study of matrices and the solution of systems of linear equations, we shall digress from our main objective long enough to present one method of solution for a single algebraic or transcendental equation in one unknown. Some familiarity with this type of problem on the part of the student is assumed.

2. THE NEWTON-RAPHSON ITERATIVE METHOD

An interesting and useful numerical method for obtaining the roots of a single equation in one unknown is due to Raphson, based upon a concept of Newton's. The method illustrates the use of successive approximations, a sequence of values $x_0, x_1, x_2, \ldots$, which converges under certain conditions to the desired root of $f(x) = 0$.

Consider choosing an approximate value x_0 for the desired root of $f(x) = 0$ on the basis of some knowledge of the function or its graph. Let ϵ denote the correction necessary to give the exact value of the root; that is,

$$f(x_0 + \epsilon) = 0. \qquad \text{5.2}$$

Upon expanding $f(x_0 + \epsilon)$ into a Taylor's series about the point x_0, we obtain

$$f(x_0 + \epsilon) = f(x_0) + \epsilon f'(x_0) + \frac{\epsilon^2}{2} f''(x_0) + \cdots + \frac{\epsilon^n}{n!} f^n(x_0) + \cdots. \qquad \text{5.3}$$

Assuming ϵ to be relatively small, we neglect those terms containing powers of ϵ higher than one. Making use of equations (5.2) and (5.3), we write

$$f(x_0) + \epsilon f'(x_0) = 0,$$

whereby

$$\epsilon = -\frac{f(x_0)}{f'(x_0)}. \qquad \text{5.4}$$

Our next approximation for the desired root is

$$x_1 = x_0 + \epsilon, \qquad \text{5.5}$$

or

$$x_1 = x_0 - \frac{f(x_0)}{f'(x_0)}. \qquad \text{5.6}$$

In general, our $(n + 1)$th approximation becomes

$$x_n = x_{n-1} - \frac{f(x_{n-1})}{f'(x_{n-1})}. \qquad \text{5.7}$$

From equation (5.7), it is evident that $f'(x)$ should be an expression which is simple to find and which does not vanish in the neighborhood of the desired root. It can be shown that if $f'(x)$ or $f''(x)$ vanishes in the neighborhood of the desired root, the approximations obtained by equation (5.7) may converge slowly, or not at all.

The Newton-Raphson method may be viewed geometrically. Consider the problem of determining the root of $f(x)$ in Figure 5.1. Let x_0 be the first approximation to the root. Now, P_0T_0 is the tangent line to $f(x)$ at the point $[x_0, f(x_0)]$. The equation of P_0T_0 is

$$y - f(x_0) = f'(x_0)(x - x_0).$$

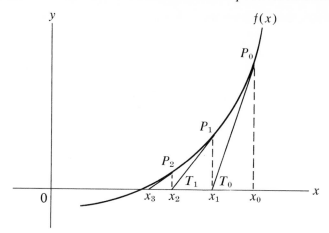

FIGURE 5.1

Letting $y = 0$, we obtain the x-intercept of the tangent line:

$$x_1 = x_0 - \frac{f(x_0)}{f'(x_0)}.$$

The tangent line to $f(x)$ at $[x_1, f(x_1)]$ is P_1T_1. In a similar manner, we may obtain the x-intercept of this tangent line:

$$x_2 = x_1 - \frac{f(x_1)}{f'(x_1)}.$$

The process may be continued. If $f'(x) \neq 0$ and $f''(x) \neq 0$ in the neighborhood of the root, it is evident that the sequence of values $x_0, x_1, x_2, \ldots$ approaches the desired root.

EXAMPLE 1.   Find an iterative formula for the rth root of a positive number.

Solution: Let N be any positive number and x its rth root. That is,

$$x^r = N, \quad \text{or} \quad x^r - N = 0.$$

Let $f(x) = x^r - N$. Then $f'(x) = rx^{r-1}$.

Now, according to equation (5.7), if we choose x_0 as an approximation for the root of the equation

$$x^r - N = 0,$$

our next approximation is given by

$$x_1 = x_0 - \frac{x_0^r - N}{rx_0^{r-1}}$$

$$= \frac{1}{r}\left[rx_0 - x_0 + \frac{N}{x_0^{r-1}}\right]$$

$$= \frac{1}{r}\left[\frac{N}{x_0^{r-1}} + (r - 1)x_0\right].$$

Successive approximations become

$$x_2 = \frac{1}{r}\left[\frac{N}{x_1^{r-1}} + (r-1)x_1\right],$$

$$x_3 = \frac{1}{r}\left[\frac{N}{x_2^{r-1}} + (r-1)x_2\right],$$

.
.
.

Hence,

$$x_{i+1} = \frac{1}{r}\left[\frac{N}{x_i^{r-1}} + (r-1)x_i\right]$$

represents an iterative formula for obtaining successive approximations to the rth root of N. Since, obviously, neither the first nor the second derivative of the function $x^r - N$ vanishes in the neighborhood of the root, the sequence of successive approximations converges to the desired root.

EXAMPLE 2.   Find the cube root of 100 to the nearest thousandth of a unit.

Solution: We choose for our first approximation $x_0 = 4$. According to the results of Example 1, our successive approximations become

$$x_1 = \frac{1}{3}\left[\frac{100}{4^2} + (2)(4)\right] = 4.75,$$

$$x_2 = \frac{1}{3}\left[\frac{100}{(4.75)^2} + (2)(4.75)\right] = 4.644,$$

$$x_3 = \frac{1}{3}\left[\frac{100}{(4.644)^2} + (2)(4.644)\right] = 4.642,$$

$$x_4 = \frac{1}{3}\left[\frac{100}{(4.642)^2} + (2)(4.642)\right] = 4.642.$$

The procedure may be terminated here since two successive approximations agree to the nearest thousandth of a unit. Hence, $\sqrt[3]{100} = 4.642$ to the nearest thousandth of a unit.

EXAMPLE 3.   Find a real positive root of

$$f(x) = 5x^3 - 3x^2 - 3x - 8.$$

Solution: By Descartes' rule of signs, we know that only one real positive root exists. Now, since $f(1) = -9$ and $f(2) = 14$, the desired root must lie between 1 and 2. Let $x_0 = 1.4$. Making use of equation (5.7),

$$x_1 = x_0 - \frac{f(x_0)}{f'(x_0)}$$

$$= x_0 - \frac{5x_0^3 - 3x_0^2 - 3x_0 - 8}{15x_0^2 - 6x_0 - 3}$$

$$= \frac{10x_0^3 - 3x_0^2 + 8}{15x_0^2 - 6x_0 - 3}$$

$$= 1.64.$$

Continuing the iterative procedure,

$$x_2 = \frac{10x_1^3 - 3x_1^2 + 8}{15x_1^2 - 6x_1 - 3}$$

$$= 1.60,$$

and

$$x_3 = \frac{10x_2^3 - 3x_2^2 + 8}{15x_2^2 - 6x_2 - 3}$$

$$= 1.60.$$

Since $x_2 = x_3$, we terminate the process, accepting 1.60 as the desired root.

EXERCISES

1. Calculate the real roots of the following equations to the nearest hundredth of a unit:

   (a) $x^3 = 5$;   (b) $x^2 = 2$;
   (c) $x^3 + 3x - 5 = 0$;   (d) $e^x + x - 3 = 0$;
   (e) $x + \log x = 2$;   (f) $\cos x = x^2$;
   (g) $x^3 - 30x - 110 = 0$;   (h) $x^4 + 8x - 12 = 0$;
   (i) $x = 2 + \sin x$;   (j) $x^2 + 4 \sin x = 0$.

2. Apply the Newton-Raphson method to the equation

   $$x^2 - N = 0$$

   and derive a well-known rule for extracting square roots. State the rule.

3. Make sketches to show that the Newton-Raphson method may not be valid if $f'(x)$ or $f''(x)$ vanishes near the root of $f(x) = 0$.

3. ELEMENTS OF MATRIX ALGEBRA

Rectangular arrays of a set of scalars or numbers such as

$$\begin{pmatrix} a_{11} & a_{12} & \cdots & a_{1n} \\ a_{21} & a_{22} & \cdots & a_{2n} \\ \cdots & \cdots & \cdots & \cdots \\ a_{m1} & a_{m2} & \cdots & a_{mn} \end{pmatrix} \qquad \text{5.8}$$

are called *matrices* (singular: *matrix*). A matrix of m rows and n columns is called a matrix of *order m by n*. A *square matrix* is a matrix for which the number of rows is equal to the number of columns, that is, $m = n$. The scalar or *element* of the ith row and jth column is designated a_{ij}.

Matrices may be denoted symbolically by use of capital letters $A, B, C, \ldots$, or by $(a_{ij}), (b_{ij}), (c_{ij}), \ldots$.

Two matrices A and B are said to be equal if they are of the same order and $a_{ij} = b_{ij}$ for all pairs i, j.

The sum of two matrices A and B of the same order is defined as a matrix C of the same order such that each element c_{ij} of C is the sum of the corresponding elements a_{ij} and b_{ij} of A and B, respectively. That is,

$$A + B = C,$$

where

$$a_{ij} + b_{ij} = c_{ij} \qquad \text{for all pairs } i, j.$$

The product of a scalar k and a matrix A is defined as a matrix whose elements are the products of k and the corresponding elements of A. That is,

$$k(a_{ij}) = (ka_{ij}) \qquad \text{for all pairs } i, j. \qquad \text{5.9}$$

The product of two matrices A and B is defined to be a matrix C such that the element in the ith row and jth column is obtained by summing the products of the elements of the ith row in A and the elements of the jth column in B, taken in order. That is,

$$c_{ij} = a_{i1}b_{1j} + a_{i2}b_{2j} + \cdots + a_{in}b_{nj} \qquad \text{5.10}$$

or, more concisely,

$$c_{ij} = \sum_{k=1}^{n} a_{ik}b_{kj}. \qquad \text{5.11}$$

It is evident from the definition of matrix multiplication that two matrices can be multiplied only when they are *conformable*; that is, the number of columns in the first matrix must be equal to the number of rows in the second matrix. If A is a matrix of order m by n and B is a matrix of order n by k, the product AB is a matrix of order m by k. The product BA will not exist unless $m = k$.

While it is immediately evident that matrix multiplication is, in general, not commutative, two other familiar laws of the algebra of real numbers hold for matrix multiplication. It can be shown that the multiplication of matrices is distributive with respect to addition. That is,

$$A(B + C) = AB + AC, \qquad\qquad \textbf{5.12}$$

and

$$(A + B)C = AC + BC. \qquad\qquad \textbf{5.13}$$

Of great importance is the fact that the product of matrices is associative. That is,

$$(AB)C = A(BC). \qquad\qquad \textbf{5.14}$$

Elements d_{ii} of a square matrix D are called the *diagonal elements* of D and are said to lie on the *main*, or *principal*, *diagonal*. A square matrix such as

$$\begin{pmatrix} d_{11} & 0 & \cdots & 0 \\ 0 & d_{22} & \cdots & 0 \\ \cdots & \cdots & \cdots & \cdots \\ 0 & 0 & \cdots & d_{nn} \end{pmatrix} \qquad\qquad \textbf{5.15}$$

is called a *diagonal matrix*. If all the d_{ii}'s are equal, the diagonal matrix is called a *scalar matrix*. A scalar matrix for which $d_{ii} = 1$ is called an *identity*, or *unit*, *matrix*. An identity matrix I has the property that

$$AI = IA = A, \qquad\qquad \textbf{5.16}$$

where A is a square matrix of the same order as I. We sometimes denote the identity matrix by (δ_{ij}), making use of the *Kronecker delta* δ_{ij}. This symbol is defined by

$$\delta_{ij} = \begin{cases} 0, & \text{when } i \neq j, \\ 1, & \text{when } i = j. \end{cases} \qquad\qquad \textbf{5.17}$$

EXAMPLE 1. Find the sum of $3A + 2B$ where

$$A = \begin{pmatrix} 3 & 0 & -1 \\ -2 & 1 & -2 \end{pmatrix} \quad \text{and} \quad B = \begin{pmatrix} 4 & 2 & 3 \\ 1 & 0 & 1 \end{pmatrix}.$$

Solution: From equation (5.9),

$$3A = \begin{pmatrix} 3 \cdot [3] & 3 \cdot [0] & 3 \cdot [-1] \\ 3 \cdot [-2] & 3 \cdot [1] & 3 \cdot [-2] \end{pmatrix} = \begin{pmatrix} 9 & 0 & -3 \\ -6 & 3 & -6 \end{pmatrix},$$

and

$$2B = \begin{pmatrix} 2 \cdot [4] & 2 \cdot [2] & 2 \cdot [3] \\ 2 \cdot [1] & 2 \cdot [0] & 2 \cdot [1] \end{pmatrix} = \begin{pmatrix} 8 & 4 & 6 \\ 2 & 0 & 2 \end{pmatrix}.$$

Now, by the definition of addition of two matrices,

$$3A + 2B = \begin{pmatrix} 9 + 8 & 0 + 4 & -3 + 6 \\ -6 + 2 & 3 + 0 & -6 + 2 \end{pmatrix} = \begin{pmatrix} 17 & 4 & 3 \\ -4 & 3 & -4 \end{pmatrix}.$$

EXAMPLE 2.   Find the products AB and BA, if they exist, where

$$A = \begin{pmatrix} 3 & 2 \\ 1 & 0 \\ -1 & 1 \end{pmatrix} \quad \text{and} \quad B = \begin{pmatrix} 4 & 0 \\ -1 & 3 \end{pmatrix}.$$

Solution: Now, A and B are conformable when taken in that order since the number of columns in A equals the number of rows in B. Hence, AB exists. Furthermore, AB is of order 3 by 2 since A is of order 3 by 2 and B is of order 2 by 2. Making use of equation (5.10), we have

$$AB = \begin{pmatrix} [3] \cdot [4] + [2] \cdot [-1] & [3] \cdot [0] + [2] \cdot [3] \\ [1] \cdot [4] + [0] \cdot [-1] & [1] \cdot [0] + [0] \cdot [3] \\ [-1] \cdot [4] + [1] \cdot [-1] & [-1] \cdot [0] + [1] \cdot [3] \end{pmatrix}$$

$$= \begin{pmatrix} 10 & 6 \\ 4 & 0 \\ -5 & 3 \end{pmatrix}.$$

The product BA does not exist since the matrices B and A are not conformable when taken in this order.

EXERCISES

1. Construct a square matrix (a_{ij}) of order 3 by 3 where $a_{ij} = i^2 - j$.
2. In the matrix (a_{ij}), where are all the elements with constant i? With constant j? With $i = j$?
3. Prove that the addition of matrices is commutative and associative.
4. Making use of the definitions of matrix addition and scalar multiplication of a matrix, evaluate $A - B$ where A and B are the matrices of Example 1.
5. Verify that the multiplication of square matrices is generally not commutative using

$$A = \begin{pmatrix} 2 & 0 & 1 \\ -1 & 2 & 3 \\ 4 & 0 & 1 \end{pmatrix} \quad \text{and} \quad B = \begin{pmatrix} 0 & 2 & 0 \\ 0 & 1 & 3 \\ 1 & 0 & 4 \end{pmatrix}.$$

6. Show that $AB = BA = I$ where

$$A = \begin{pmatrix} 1 & -1 & 1 \\ 0 & 1 & 0 \\ 2 & 0 & 3 \end{pmatrix} \quad \text{and} \quad B = \begin{pmatrix} 3 & 3 & -1 \\ 0 & 1 & 0 \\ -2 & -2 & 1 \end{pmatrix}.$$

7. Determine under what conditions

$$(A + B)(A - B) = A^2 - B^2.$$

8. Verify equations (5.12) and (5.13) for the matrices

$$A = \begin{pmatrix} 2 & 1 \\ -3 & 4 \end{pmatrix}, \quad B = \begin{pmatrix} 1 & -1 \\ 2 & 0 \end{pmatrix}, \quad \text{and} \quad C = \begin{pmatrix} 3 & 1 \\ -1 & 2 \end{pmatrix}.$$

9. Verify equation (5.14) where

$$A = \begin{pmatrix} 2 & 0 & -1 \\ -1 & 3 & 1 \end{pmatrix}, \quad B = \begin{pmatrix} 1 & 2 & 0 \\ -1 & 3 & 4 \\ 1 & 2 & -1 \end{pmatrix}, \quad \text{and} \quad C = \begin{pmatrix} 0 & 1 \\ 2 & 1 \\ 0 & 4 \end{pmatrix}.$$

10. Can the product of two nonsquare matrices be a square matrix? If so, when? If not, why not?

11. A *null*, or *zero*, *matrix*, denoted by 0, is defined as that matrix for which $A + 0 = A$. All of its elements are necessarily zero. Verify that if $AB = 0$, neither A nor B must necessarily be a null matrix using

$$A = \begin{pmatrix} 1 & 0 \\ 0 & 0 \end{pmatrix} \quad \text{and} \quad B = \begin{pmatrix} 0 & 0 \\ 0 & 1 \end{pmatrix}.$$

12. Find AB and BA where

$$A = (x \quad y \quad z) \quad \text{and} \quad B = \begin{pmatrix} x \\ y \\ z \end{pmatrix}.$$

13. Prove that the product of two square diagonal matrices of the same order is commutative.

14. What is the effect of premultiplication and postmultiplication of a square matrix by a conformable square diagonal matrix? By a scalar matrix?

15. If

$$\begin{pmatrix} x_1 \\ x_2 \end{pmatrix} = \begin{pmatrix} a & b \\ c & d \end{pmatrix}\begin{pmatrix} y_1 \\ y_2 \end{pmatrix} \quad \text{and} \quad \begin{pmatrix} y_1 \\ y_2 \end{pmatrix} = \begin{pmatrix} e & f \\ g & h \end{pmatrix}\begin{pmatrix} z_1 \\ z_2 \end{pmatrix},$$

find x_1 and x_2 in terms of z_1 and z_2.

16. Show that the matrix

$$A = \begin{pmatrix} 2 & 3 \\ -1 & 1 \end{pmatrix}$$

satisfies the equation

$$\begin{vmatrix} 2 - \lambda & 3 \\ -1 & 1 - \lambda \end{vmatrix} = 0$$

if λ is replaced by the matrix A and each scalar c is replaced by

$$c\begin{pmatrix} 1 & 0 \\ 0 & 1 \end{pmatrix}.$$

17. A matrix obtained by interchanging the rows and columns of a given matrix A is called the *transpose* of A and is denoted by A'. Prove the following for all matrices A and B:

(a) $(A')' = A$;

(b) $(A + B)' = A' + B'$;

(c) $(AB)' = B'A'$.

18. Verify the results of Exercise 17(c) for

$$A = \begin{pmatrix} 4 & 0 \\ 3 & -2 \\ 1 & 2 \end{pmatrix} \quad \text{and} \quad B = \begin{pmatrix} 1 & 0 & -1 & 2 \\ 3 & 1 & 2 & -1 \end{pmatrix}.$$

19. A matrix (a_{ij}) is said to be *symmetric* if $a_{ij} = a_{ji}$ for all pairs of values of i, j. Show the following:

(a) All symmetric matrices are square.

(b) The transpose of a symmetric matrix is equal to the matrix.

(c) The product of a matrix and its transpose is a symmetric matrix.

20. Verify the results of Exercise 19(c) for

$$A = \begin{pmatrix} 1 & 2 & -1 \\ 0 & 3 & 4 \end{pmatrix}.$$

4. THE INVERSE OF A MATRIX

Consider any square matrix (a_{ij}) and its associated determinant $|a_{ij}|$. The determinant obtained from $|a_{ij}|$ by deleting the elements of the ith row and jth column is called the *minor* of the element a_{ij} and shall be denoted by M_{ij}. The minor, prefixed with a positive or negative sign according to whether the sum of the numbers of the row and column deleted from $|a_{ij}|$ is even or odd, respectively, is called the *cofactor* of the element a_{ij} and shall be denoted by the symbol A_{ij}. That is,

$$A_{ij} = (-1)^{i+j} M_{ij}. \qquad \textbf{5.18}$$

For example, the minor of a_{12} in

$$A = \begin{pmatrix} a_{11} & a_{12} & a_{13} \\ a_{21} & a_{22} & a_{23} \\ a_{31} & a_{32} & a_{33} \end{pmatrix}$$

is

$$M_{12} = \begin{vmatrix} a_{21} & a_{23} \\ a_{31} & a_{33} \end{vmatrix},$$

and the cofactor is

$$A_{12} = (-1)^{1+2} M_{12} = -\begin{vmatrix} a_{21} & a_{23} \\ a_{31} & a_{33} \end{vmatrix}.$$

From a study of determinants,† we know that any determinant is equal to the sum of the products of the elements of a row (or column) by their cofactors. That is,

$$|A| = \sum_{j=1}^{n} a_{ij}A_{ij} \qquad \text{for any } i, \qquad\qquad \textbf{5.19}$$

and

$$|A| = \sum_{i=1}^{n} a_{ij}A_{ij} \qquad \text{for any } j. \qquad\qquad \textbf{5.20}$$

This is usually referred to as the *expansion of the determinant by minors.* In addition, it is obvious that

$$\sum_{j=1}^{n} a_{hj}A_{ij} = 0 \qquad \text{for any } h, i \text{ where } h \neq i, \qquad\qquad \textbf{5.21}$$

and

$$\sum_{i=1}^{n} a_{ih}A_{ij} = 0 \qquad \text{for any } h, j \text{ where } h \neq j, \qquad\qquad \textbf{5.22}$$

since these equations are equivalent to the expansion of a determinant in which two rows or columns are identical.

We may combine equations (5.19) through (5.22) as follows:

$$\sum_{j=1}^{n} a_{hj}A_{ij} = \delta_{hi}|A| \qquad \text{where } h, i = 1, 2, \ldots, n. \qquad\qquad \textbf{5.23}$$

and

$$\sum_{i=1}^{n} a_{ih}A_{ij} = \delta_{hj}|A| \qquad \text{where } h, j = 1, 2, \ldots, n. \qquad\qquad \textbf{5.24}$$

Now, all the possible equations of (5.23) may be written in the matrix form

$$(a_{ij})(A_{ij})' = (\delta_{ij})|A|. \qquad\qquad \textbf{5.25}$$

We shall define the transpose of the matrix obtained by replacing each element of a square matrix A by its cofactors as the *adjoint* of matrix A, and denote it by $\bar{A}$ or $\overline{(a_{ij})}$. Briefly stated, the adjoint of A is the transpose of the matrix of the cofactors of A. Equation (5.25) may now be written in the form

$$A\bar{A} = I|A|, \qquad\qquad \textbf{5.26}$$

or

$$A\frac{\bar{A}}{|A|} = I. \qquad\qquad \textbf{5.27}$$

The matrix $\dfrac{\bar{A}}{|A|}$ is called the *inverse* of A, and shall be denoted symbolically by A^{-1}. That is,

$$AA^{-1} = I. \qquad\qquad \textbf{5.28}$$

† See Appendix for a brief discussion of determinants.

In order for the inverse to exist, note that $|A| \neq 0$. Matrices for which $|A| \neq 0$ are said to be *nonsingular*. If $|A| = 0$, then A is said to be *singular*.

The n^2 possible equations of (5.24) may be written in matrix notation as

$$A'(A_{ij}) = |A|\, I. \qquad\qquad 5.29$$

Taking the transpose of both sides, we have

$$\bar{A}A = |A|\, I, \qquad\qquad 5.30$$

or

$$\frac{\bar{A}}{|A|} A = I. \qquad\qquad 5.31$$

Hence,

$$A^{-1}A = I. \qquad\qquad 5.32$$

Therefore, if it exists, the inverse of a square matrix A is commutative with A. That is,

$$AA^{-1} = A^{-1}A = I. \qquad\qquad 5.33$$

We have shown that the inverse of a matrix is the quotient of the adjoint of the matrix (transpose of the cofactor matrix) and the determinant of the matrix. This inverse is defined only for square matrices. Furthermore, it can be shown that the inverse of a matrix is unique, when it exists. Consider the following: If $AB = AC = I$, since A is nonsingular, there exists an A^{-1} such that $A^{-1}A = I$. Therefore,

$$A^{-1}(AB) = A^{-1}(AC).$$

Making use of the associative property of matrix multiplication,

$$(A^{-1}A)B = (A^{-1}A)C.$$

Hence, $B = C$.

EXAMPLE.   Determine A^{-1} if

$$A = \begin{pmatrix} 0 & 1 & 3 \\ -2 & 3 & 9 \\ 1 & -2 & -5 \end{pmatrix}.$$

Solution: The cofactors of A are

$$A_{11} = \begin{vmatrix} 3 & 9 \\ -2 & -5 \end{vmatrix}; \quad A_{12} = -\begin{vmatrix} -2 & 9 \\ 1 & -5 \end{vmatrix}; \quad A_{13} = \begin{vmatrix} -2 & 3 \\ 1 & -2 \end{vmatrix};$$

$$A_{21} = -\begin{vmatrix} 1 & 3 \\ -2 & -5 \end{vmatrix}; \quad A_{22} = \begin{vmatrix} 0 & 3 \\ 1 & -5 \end{vmatrix}; \quad A_{23} = -\begin{vmatrix} 0 & 1 \\ 1 & -2 \end{vmatrix};$$

$$A_{31} = \begin{vmatrix} 1 & 3 \\ 3 & 9 \end{vmatrix}; \quad A_{32} = -\begin{vmatrix} 0 & 3 \\ -2 & 9 \end{vmatrix}; \quad A_{33} = \begin{vmatrix} 0 & 1 \\ -2 & 3 \end{vmatrix}.$$

We now determine the matrix of cofactors which is

$$(A_{ij}) = \begin{pmatrix} A_{11} & A_{12} & A_{13} \\ A_{21} & A_{22} & A_{23} \\ A_{31} & A_{32} & A_{33} \end{pmatrix} = \begin{pmatrix} 3 & -1 & 1 \\ -1 & -3 & 1 \\ 0 & -6 & 2 \end{pmatrix}.$$

The transpose of the matrix of cofactors, or the adjoint of A, is

$$\bar{A} = (A_{ij})' = \begin{pmatrix} 3 & -1 & 0 \\ -1 & -3 & -6 \\ 1 & 1 & 2 \end{pmatrix}.$$

Now, $A^{-1} = \dfrac{\bar{A}}{|A|}$, where

$$|A| = \begin{vmatrix} 0 & 1 & 3 \\ -2 & 3 & 9 \\ 1 & -2 & -5 \end{vmatrix} = 2.$$

Hence,

$$A^{-1} = \begin{pmatrix} \frac{3}{2} & -\frac{1}{2} & 0 \\ -\frac{1}{2} & -\frac{3}{2} & -3 \\ \frac{1}{2} & \frac{1}{2} & 1 \end{pmatrix}.$$

Check:

$$AA^{-1} = \begin{pmatrix} 0 & 1 & 3 \\ -2 & 3 & 9 \\ 1 & -2 & -5 \end{pmatrix} \begin{pmatrix} \frac{3}{2} & -\frac{1}{2} & 0 \\ -\frac{1}{2} & -\frac{3}{2} & -3 \\ \frac{1}{2} & \frac{1}{2} & 1 \end{pmatrix}$$

$$= \begin{pmatrix} 1 & 0 & 0 \\ 0 & 1 & 0 \\ 0 & 0 & 1 \end{pmatrix}$$

$$= I.$$

EXERCISES

1. Determine the inverses, if they exist, for

$$\begin{pmatrix} 8 & 5 \\ 12 & 8 \end{pmatrix}; \quad \begin{pmatrix} 1 & 2 \\ 0 & 0 \end{pmatrix}; \quad \begin{pmatrix} a & b \\ c & d \end{pmatrix}; \quad \text{and} \quad \begin{pmatrix} 2 & 1 & 1 \\ 2 & 0 & 2 \\ 0 & 1 & -3 \end{pmatrix}.$$

2. Show that

$$\begin{pmatrix} a & 0 & 0 \\ 0 & b & 0 \\ 0 & 0 & c \end{pmatrix}^{-1} = \begin{pmatrix} a^{-1} & 0 & 0 \\ 0 & b^{-1} & 0 \\ 0 & 0 & c^{-1} \end{pmatrix}.$$

3. Show that the sum of the products of the elements of the second row and the cofactors of the first row, or third row, is zero for the matrix

$$\begin{pmatrix} 3 & 4 & 0 \\ -1 & 2 & 1 \\ 2 & 1 & -2 \end{pmatrix}.$$

4. Prove that $(A^{-1})^{-1} = A$.

5. Prove that $(AB)^{-1} = B^{-1}A^{-1}$.

6. Verify Exercise 5 for

$$A = \begin{pmatrix} 2 & 0 & 2 \\ 2 & 0 & 1 \\ 0 & 1 & 0 \end{pmatrix} \quad \text{and} \quad B = \begin{pmatrix} 3 & 0 & 1 \\ -1 & -1 & 0 \\ 2 & 0 & 0 \end{pmatrix}.$$

7. Given A^{-1} is the inverse of A, find the inverse of A^2.

8. Given $AB = BA$, prove that $A^{-1}B^{-1} = B^{-1}A^{-1}$.

5. CRAMER'S RULE

Consider a system of n linear equations in n unknowns $x_1, x_2, \ldots, x_n$:

$$\begin{cases} a_{11}x_1 + a_{12}x_2 + \cdots + a_{1n}x_n = c_1, \\ a_{21}x_1 + a_{22}x_2 + \cdots + a_{2n}x_n = c_2, \\ \cdots \\ a_{n1}x_1 + a_{n2}x_2 + \cdots + a_{nn}x_n = c_n. \end{cases}$$

Such a system of equations can be written in matrix form as

$$\begin{pmatrix} a_{11} & a_{12} & \cdots & a_{1n} \\ a_{21} & a_{22} & \cdots & a_{2n} \\ \cdots & \cdots & \cdots & \cdots \\ a_{n1} & a_{n2} & \cdots & a_{nn} \end{pmatrix} \begin{pmatrix} x_1 \\ x_2 \\ \cdots \\ x_n \end{pmatrix} = \begin{pmatrix} c_1 \\ c_2 \\ \cdots \\ c_n \end{pmatrix} \qquad \textbf{5.34}$$

or, more concisely,

$$AX = C \qquad \textbf{5.35}$$

where A is the square matrix of coefficients, X is the column matrix of the unknowns, and C is the column matrix of the constants. As a consequence of our discussion of inverse matrices, if A is nonsingular ($|A| \neq 0$), then a unique solution is guaranteed. Multiplying both sides of (5.35) by A^{-1}, that solution may be written as

$$X = A^{-1}C, \qquad \textbf{5.36}$$

or

$$X = \frac{\bar{A}}{|A|} C. \qquad \textbf{5.37}$$

Equation (5.36) indicates a direct method of solving a system of linear equations by application of the inverse of the coefficient matrix. In more detail, equation (5.37) appears as

$$\begin{pmatrix} x_1 \\ x_2 \\ \cdots \\ x_n \end{pmatrix} = \frac{1}{|A|} \begin{pmatrix} A_{11} & A_{21} & \cdots & A_{n1} \\ A_{12} & A_{22} & \cdots & A_{n2} \\ \cdots & \cdots & \cdots & \cdots \\ A_{1n} & A_{2n} & \cdots & A_{nn} \end{pmatrix} \begin{pmatrix} c_1 \\ c_2 \\ \cdots \\ c_n \end{pmatrix},$$

or

$$\begin{pmatrix} x_1 \\ x_2 \\ \cdots \\ x_n \end{pmatrix} = \frac{1}{|A|} \begin{pmatrix} c_1 A_{11} + c_2 A_{21} + \cdots + c_n A_{n1} \\ c_1 A_{12} + c_2 A_{22} + \cdots + c_n A_{n2} \\ \cdots \cdots \cdots \cdots \cdots \cdots \cdots \\ c_1 A_{1n} + c_2 A_{2n} + \cdots + c_n A_{nn} \end{pmatrix}. \qquad \textbf{5.38}$$

Now, the value of each unknown x_i may be found by the formula

$$x_i = \frac{c_1 A_{1i} + c_2 A_{2i} + \cdots + c_n A_{ni}}{|A|}, \qquad \textbf{5.39}$$

or

$$x_i = \frac{\sum_{j=1}^{n} c_j A_{ji}}{|A|} \qquad \text{for } i = 1, 2, \ldots, n. \qquad \textbf{5.40}$$

The numerator on the right-hand side of equation (5.40) is the determinant of the coefficient matrix with the elements of the ith column replaced by the elements of the column matrix of constants. If we denote these determinants by $|A_1^c|$, $|A_2^c|, \ldots, |A_n^c|$ for $i = 1, 2, \ldots, n$, then (5.40) becomes

$$x_i = \frac{|A_i^c|}{|A|}. \qquad \textbf{5.41}$$

Formula (5.41) for solving a system of n linear equations in n unknowns is known as *Cramer's Rule*.

Although the rule gives a systematic procedure for solving the system of equations, it is of no practical value. High-speed digital computing machines usually employ more efficient methods for numerical solutions when n is large.

EXAMPLE.   Solve by Cramer's Rule:

$$\begin{cases} x_1 + x_2 - x_3 = 7, \\ 2x_1 + 3x_2 + x_3 = 3, \\ 3x_1 - 4x_2 - 2x_3 = 10. \end{cases}$$

Solution: The determinant of the coefficient matrix is

$$|A| = \begin{vmatrix} 1 & 1 & -1 \\ 2 & 3 & 1 \\ 3 & -4 & -2 \end{vmatrix} = 22.$$

Since $|A|$ is nonvanishing, a unique solution exists. Using equation (5.41),

$$x_1 = \frac{\begin{vmatrix} 7 & 1 & -1 \\ 3 & 3 & 1 \\ 10 & -4 & -2 \end{vmatrix}}{22} = \frac{44}{22} = 2,$$

$$x_2 = \frac{\begin{vmatrix} 1 & 7 & -1 \\ 2 & 3 & 1 \\ 3 & 10 & -2 \end{vmatrix}}{22} = \frac{22}{22} = 1,$$

and

$$x_3 = \frac{\begin{vmatrix} 1 & 1 & 7 \\ 2 & 3 & 3 \\ 3 & -4 & 10 \end{vmatrix}}{22} = -\frac{88}{22} = -4.$$

EXERCISES

1.   Solve the following systems of linear equations by Cramer's Rule:

(a) $\begin{cases} x + 2y - 3z = 1, \\ x - 3y + z = 2, \\ 2x + 9y - 4z = 1; \end{cases}$

(b) $\begin{cases} w + x + y - z = 2, \\ w + x + y + z = 1, \\ w - x + y + z = 4, \\ w + x - y + z = 3; \end{cases}$

(c) $\begin{cases} 2w + x - y + 7z = -2, \\ 6w - 5x + 3y + 5z = -10, \\ 8w + 2x - y - 3z = 15, \\ 4w + 3x - 2y - z = 12; \end{cases}$

(d) $\begin{cases} 2y + z = 0, \\ -x + 3y + 5z = 0, \\ 3x + 4y - z = 0. \end{cases}$

2. Prove that there exist unique constants A, B, and C such that

$$\frac{ax^2 + bx + c}{(x - r_1)(x - r_2)(x - r_3)} = \frac{A}{x - r_1} + \frac{B}{x - r_2} + \frac{C}{x - r_3}.$$

3. Solve the system of linear equations:

$$\begin{cases} x_1 + 2x_2 - x_3 = 5, \\ 2x_1 + x_3 + x_4 = -3, \\ x_1 + 2x_2 + x_4 = 4, \\ x_2 - x_3 - 2x_4 = 5. \end{cases}$$

4. Solve the following sets of simultaneous linear equations and interpret the systems geometrically:

(a) $\begin{cases} 2x - y + 3 = 0, \\ x + 2y - 6 = 0; \end{cases}$ (b) $\begin{cases} x - 2y = 5, \\ 3x - y = 5; \end{cases}$

(c) $\begin{cases} x + 3y = -2, \\ 3x + 9y = -6; \end{cases}$ (d) $\begin{cases} x + 2y = 2, \\ 2x + 4y = -5; \end{cases}$

(e) $\begin{cases} 3bx - 3ay = 4b^2, \\ x + 3y = 4b + a; \end{cases}$ (f) $\begin{cases} x + 2by = a^2 + b^2, \\ x - by = a^2 - b^2. \end{cases}$

5. The functions $e_1, e_2, \ldots, e_n$ are said to be *linearly dependent* if there exists a combination of them $k_1 e_1 + k_2 e_2 + \cdots + k_n e_n = 0$ where not all k_i's equal zero. Determine if $f(x, y, z)$, $g(x, y, z)$, and $h(x, y, z)$ are linearly dependent functions where

$$f(x, y, z) = x - y + z,$$
$$g(x, y, z) = x + y + 2z,$$
$$h(x, y, z) = 3x + y + 5z.$$

6. If a set of n functions are linearly dependent, show that at least one function is a linear combination of the others.

6. GAUSS' ELIMINATION METHOD

The methods of solution of a system of n linear equations, $AX = C$, discussed so far, involve either the calculation and application of A^{-1} or the evaluation of $n + 1$ determinants. In each case, as the system becomes larger, the computational problem becomes more complex. A relatively simple, systematic procedure, well-adapted to desk calculators and large-scale digital computers, will be presented in this section.

Consider a system of n linear equations in n unknowns expressed by (5.1) or, in matrix form, by (5.34). In addition to the matrix of coefficients

$$\begin{pmatrix} a_{11} & a_{12} & \cdots & a_{1n} \\ a_{21} & a_{22} & \cdots & a_{2n} \\ \cdots & \cdots & \cdots & \cdots \\ a_{n1} & a_{n2} & \cdots & a_{nn} \end{pmatrix}, \qquad \textbf{5.42}$$

we shall define the matrix composed of the elements of (5.42) with the constants $c_1, c_2, \ldots, c_n$ included as an additional column to be the *augmented matrix* of the system. That is,

$$\begin{pmatrix} a_{11} & a_{12} & \cdots & a_{1n} & c_1 \\ a_{21} & a_{22} & \cdots & a_{2n} & c_2 \\ \cdots & \cdots & \cdots & \cdots & \cdots \\ a_{n1} & a_{n2} & \cdots & a_{nn} & c_n \end{pmatrix}$$

5.43

is the augmented matrix of (5.1).

In finding solutions, if they exist, to a system of linear equations, certain simple operations may be employed to convert the system to an equivalent system. An equivalent system is certainly obtained if:

1. Two equations are interchanged.

2. Any equation is multiplied by a nonzero scalar.

3. A nonzero scalar multiple of one equation is added to another equation of the system.

Consider, for the moment, a system of three linear equations in three unknowns

$$\begin{pmatrix} a_{11} & a_{12} & a_{13} \\ a_{21} & a_{22} & a_{23} \\ a_{31} & a_{32} & a_{33} \end{pmatrix} \begin{pmatrix} x_1 \\ x_2 \\ x_3 \end{pmatrix} = \begin{pmatrix} c_1 \\ c_2 \\ c_3 \end{pmatrix}$$

with augmented matrix

$$\begin{pmatrix} a_{11} & a_{12} & a_{13} & c_1 \\ a_{21} & a_{22} & a_{23} & c_2 \\ a_{31} & a_{32} & a_{33} & c_3 \end{pmatrix}.$$

Essentially, the solution of the system consists of performing the three operations mentioned above until the array

$$\begin{pmatrix} 1 & 0 & 0 \\ 0 & 1 & 0 \\ 0 & 0 & 1 \end{pmatrix} \begin{pmatrix} x_1 \\ x_2 \\ x_3 \end{pmatrix} = \begin{pmatrix} k_1 \\ k_2 \\ k_3 \end{pmatrix}$$

is obtained, indicating k_1, k_2, k_3 as solutions of the system. The augmented matrix of the system now appears in the form

$$\begin{pmatrix} 1 & 0 & 0 & k_1 \\ 0 & 1 & 0 & k_2 \\ 0 & 0 & 1 & k_3 \end{pmatrix}.$$

5.44

Therefore, the solutions of the system may be obtained by considering only the augmented matrix. We must attempt to reduce it to this *diagonal form* by performing three *elementary row transformations* on the matrix as follows:

1. The interchange of two rows.

2. Multiplication of the elements of any row by a nonzero scalar.

3. Addition of a nonzero scalar multiple of the elements of any row onto the corresponding elements of another row.

A modified form of this procedure and one which requires fewer elementary row transformations involves reducing the augmented matrix to the *triangular form:*

$$\begin{pmatrix} 1 & \alpha_{12} & \alpha_{13} & \beta_1 \\ 0 & 1 & \alpha_{23} & \beta_2 \\ 0 & 0 & 1 & \beta_3 \end{pmatrix},$$

which represents the equivalent linear system

$$x_1 + \alpha_{12}x_2 + \alpha_{13}x_3 = \beta_1,$$
$$x_2 + \alpha_{23}x_3 = \beta_2,$$
$$x_3 = \beta_3.$$

The solution set can now be found by substitution, starting from the last equation and working back to the first equation.

A systematic procedure which we may follow to obtain the triangular form of the augmented matrix by means of the elementary row transformations is known as *Gauss' elimination method*. Considering the augmented matrix for a system of n linear equations in n unknowns represented by (5.43), perform a sequence of transformations on (5.43) by multiplying the elements of row one by

$$-\frac{a_{i1}}{a_{11}} \qquad \text{for } i = 2, 3, \ldots, n$$

and adding the products to the corresponding elements of the ith row. Then multiply the elements of row one by $\dfrac{1}{a_{11}}$. If $a_{11} = 0$, the process we are following may be accomplished after an interchange of rows enabling the element in the original position of a_{11} to be nonzero. A similar exchange is assumed throughout the process being described whenever division by zero might occur. The form of the augmented matrix now becomes

$$\begin{pmatrix} 1 & \alpha_{12} & \alpha_{13} & \cdots & \alpha_{1n} & c_1' \\ 0 & \alpha_{22} & \alpha_{23} & \cdots & \alpha_{2n} & c_2' \\ 0 & \alpha_{32} & \alpha_{33} & \cdots & \alpha_{3n} & c_3' \\ \cdots & \cdots & \cdots & \cdots & \cdots & \cdots \\ 0 & \alpha_{n2} & \alpha_{n3} & \cdots & \alpha_{nn} & c_n' \end{pmatrix}.$$

Perform another sequence of transformations on this augmented matrix by multiplying the elements of row two by

$$-\frac{\alpha_{i2}}{\alpha_{22}} \qquad \text{for } i = 3, 4, \ldots, n$$

and adding the products to the corresponding elements of the ith row. Then multiply the elements of row two by $\frac{1}{\alpha_{22}}$. The form of the equivalent augmented matrix becomes

$$\begin{pmatrix} 1 & \alpha_{12} & \alpha_{13} & \cdots & \alpha_{1n} & c_1' \\ 0 & 1 & \beta_{23} & \cdots & \beta_{2n} & c_2'' \\ 0 & 0 & \beta_{33} & \cdots & \beta_{3n} & c_3'' \\ \cdots & \cdots & \cdots & \cdots & \cdots & \cdots \\ 0 & 0 & \beta_{n3} & \cdots & \beta_{nn} & c_n'' \end{pmatrix}.$$

Now, after a sequence of n similar transformations, the augmented matrix takes on the desired triangular form

$$\begin{pmatrix} 1 & \alpha_{12} & \alpha_{13} & \cdots & \alpha_{1n} & c_1' \\ 0 & 1 & \beta_{23} & \cdots & \beta_{2n} & c_2'' \\ 0 & 0 & 1 & \cdots & \gamma_{3n} & c_3''' \\ \cdots & \cdots & \cdots & \cdots & \cdots & \cdots \\ 0 & 0 & 0 & \cdots & 1 & c_n^n \end{pmatrix}.$$

EXAMPLE 1.   Solve the system of equations:

$$\begin{cases} x_1 - x_2 + 3x_3 = 3, \\ 3x_1 - 4x_2 - x_3 = 1, \\ -3x_1 + 2x_2 + 2x_3 = 4. \end{cases}$$

Solution: The augmented matrix of this system is

$$\begin{pmatrix} 1 & -1 & 3 & 3 \\ 3 & -4 & -1 & 1 \\ -3 & 2 & 2 & 4 \end{pmatrix}.$$

Multiplying the elements of row one by the scalar -3 and adding the results to the corresponding elements of row two, we have

$$\begin{pmatrix} 1 & -1 & 3 & 3 \\ 0 & -1 & -10 & -8 \\ -3 & 2 & 2 & 4 \end{pmatrix}.$$

Similarly, by multiplying the elements of row one by the scalar 3 and adding the results to the corresponding elements of row three, the augmented matrix becomes

$$\begin{pmatrix} 1 & -1 & 3 & 3 \\ 0 & -1 & -10 & -8 \\ 0 & -1 & 11 & 13 \end{pmatrix}.$$

After multiplying the elements of row two by -1 and adding to the corresponding elements of row three, we have

$$\begin{pmatrix} 1 & -1 & 3 & 3 \\ 0 & -1 & -10 & -8 \\ 0 & 0 & 21 & 21 \end{pmatrix}.$$

Multiplication of the elements of rows two and three by -1 and $\dfrac{1}{21}$, respectively, places the augmented matrix in the desired triangular form

$$\begin{pmatrix} 1 & -1 & 3 & 3 \\ 0 & 1 & 10 & 8 \\ 0 & 0 & 1 & 1 \end{pmatrix}.$$

Now, this augmented matrix represents the equivalent linear system

$$\begin{cases} x_1 - x_2 + 3x_3 = 3, \\ x_2 + 10x_3 = 8, \\ x_3 = 1. \end{cases}$$

Since $x_3 = 1$ from the last equation, substituting in the second equation, we have

$$x_2 + 10 = 8;$$

that is, $x_2 = -2.$

Substituting 1 and -2 for x_1 and x_2, respectively, in the first equation,

$$x_1 + 2 + 3 = 3;$$

that is, $x_1 = -2.$

Hence, the solution set consists of

$$x_1 = -2,$$
$$x_2 = -2,$$

and

$$x_3 = 1.$$

EXAMPLE 2.   Transform the following system of equations to an equivalent system in triangular form:

$$\begin{cases} x - y + z = 2, \\ 2x + y - z = 1, \\ 3x + y - z = 0. \end{cases}$$

Solution: The augmented matrix is

$$\begin{pmatrix} 1 & -1 & 1 & 2 \\ 2 & 1 & -1 & 1 \\ 3 & 1 & -1 & 0 \end{pmatrix}.$$

Proceeding in the manner described in Example 1, the augmented matrix takes on the following forms in the sequence indicated:

$$\begin{pmatrix} 1 & -1 & 1 & 2 \\ 0 & 3 & -3 & -3 \\ 3 & 1 & -1 & 0 \end{pmatrix},$$

$$\begin{pmatrix} 1 & -1 & 1 & 2 \\ 0 & 3 & -3 & -3 \\ 0 & 4 & -4 & -6 \end{pmatrix},$$

$$\begin{pmatrix} 1 & -1 & 1 & 2 \\ 0 & 3 & -3 & -3 \\ 0 & 0 & 0 & -2 \end{pmatrix},$$

$$\begin{pmatrix} 1 & -1 & 1 & 2 \\ 0 & 1 & -1 & -1 \\ 0 & 0 & 0 & -2 \end{pmatrix}.$$

Now, remember that the augmented matrix represents the system of equations

$$\begin{cases} x_1 - x_2 + x_3 = 2, \\ x_2 - x_3 = -1, \\ 0 = -2. \end{cases}$$

However, since $0 \neq -2$, the system of equations must be *inconsistent* (does not have a solution).

EXAMPLE 3. The equivalent triangular form of the system of equations

$$\begin{cases} x_1 - x_2 - x_3 = 1, \\ 3x_1 - 4x_2 - 2x_3 = 1, \\ -x_1 + 3x_2 - x_3 = 3, \end{cases}$$

can be shown to be

$$\begin{cases} x_1 - x_2 - x_3 = 1, \\ x_2 - x_3 = 2, \\ 0 = 0. \end{cases}$$

Discuss the solution set.

Solution: Now, $x_2 = 2 + x_3$,

and $x_1 = 3 + 2x_3$.

Hence, there exists an infinite number of solutions. The value of one variable, say x_3, may be chosen arbitrarily, thus fixing the values of the remaining two variables. Letting $x_3 = t$, an arbitrary real number, we have

$$\begin{cases} x_1 = 3 + 2t, \\ x_2 = 2 + t, \\ x_3 = t, \end{cases}$$

as the form of our family of solutions. Although no unique solution exists, the system is still said to be *consistent*; that is, a solution exists.

It should be noted that the transformation of a system of linear equations to an equivalent triangular form will give immediate information about the system even when it does not have a unique solution. In addition, it should be mentioned here that Gauss' elimination method is applicable to systems of linear equations in which the number of equations and the number of unknowns are not the same. However, a detailed analysis of this problem is beyond the scope of our objectives.

EXERCISES

1. Use Gauss' elimination method to determine the solution sets, if they exist, for the following systems of equations:

(a) $\begin{cases} 2x_1 - 4x_2 + 5x_3 = 10, \\ 2x_1 - 11x_2 + 10x_3 = 36, \\ 4x_1 - x_2 + 5x_3 = -6; \end{cases}$

(b) $\begin{cases} x_1 + x_2 + x_3 - x_4 = 0, \\ 2x_1 - 3x_2 - 2x_3 + 2x_4 = 19, \\ x_1 + 3x_2 + 2x_3 - 2x_4 = -4, \\ 3x_1 + x_2 - x_3 = -3; \end{cases}$

(c) $\begin{cases} x_1 - 2x_2 + x_3 = 5, \\ 2x_1 - 5x_1 + 6x_3 = -2, \\ x_1 + x_2 - 2x_3 = 3; \end{cases}$

(d) $\begin{cases} 2x_1 + 2x_2 + 5x_3 = 1, \\ 8x_1 - 2x_2 + x_3 = 5, \\ 4x_1 - 5x_2 - 2x_3 = 8; \end{cases}$

(e) $\begin{cases} x_1 + 2x_2 + x_3 = 5, \\ x_1 - x_2 - 2x_3 = 6; \end{cases}$ (f) $\begin{cases} 3x_1 - 7x_2 + 2x_3 = 0, \\ 2x_1 - 7x_2 - x_3 = 0; \end{cases}$

(g) $\begin{cases} 2x_1 + x_2 + x_3 = -3, \\ x_1 - x_2 + 2x_3 = 0, \\ 3x_1 - 3x_2 + 4x_3 = -6, \\ x_1 + x_2 - x_3 = 10; \end{cases}$ (h) $\begin{cases} x_1 - x_2 + 2x_3 = 3, \\ x_1 - x_2 + x_3 = 3, \\ x_1 - x_2 - x_3 = -1; \end{cases}$

(i) $\begin{cases} 2x_1 + 3x_2 + x_3 = 0, \\ x_1 + 4x_2 + 2x_3 = 0, \\ 3x_1 - x_2 = 0; \end{cases}$ (j) $\begin{cases} x_1 + x_2 + x_3 + x_4 + x_5 = 3, \\ 2x_1 - 4x_2 + 3x_3 + 3x_4 - x_5 = -1, \\ 3x_1 - x_2 - x_3 - x_4 + 2x_5 = 13, \\ -x_1 + x_2 - x_3 - x_4 + x_5 = 3, \\ 4x_1 + 2x_2 - x_3 + x_4 + 3x_5 = 9. \end{cases}$

2.   Determine the values of k such that the following systems of equations will be consistent:

(a) $\begin{cases} 2x_1 + x_2 + x_3 = 5, \\ x_1 - x_2 + 3x_3 = 2, \\ 3x_1 + 3x_2 - x_3 = k; \end{cases}$ (b) $\begin{cases} x_1 + x_2 + x_3 = 1, \\ x_1 - x_2 + x_3 = 1, \\ x_1 + x_2 - x_3 = k. \end{cases}$

3.   Find the products AB where

$$A = \begin{pmatrix} 0 & 1 & 0 \\ 1 & 0 & 0 \\ 0 & 0 & 1 \end{pmatrix}; \quad \begin{pmatrix} k & 0 & 0 \\ 0 & 1 & 0 \\ 0 & 0 & 1 \end{pmatrix}; \quad \text{and} \quad \begin{pmatrix} 1 & 0 & 0 \\ k & 1 & 0 \\ 0 & 0 & 1 \end{pmatrix}$$

and B is a general square matrix of order 3 by 3. Discuss the results in terms of the elementary row transformations.

4.   What is the maximum number of elementary row transformations necessary to reduce a square matrix of order n by n to diagonal form? Triangular form?

5.   A system of linear equations in the matrix form $AX = 0$ is called a system of *homogeneous* linear equations. Show that such a system is necessarily consistent.

7. CHOLESKY'S METHOD

When the matrix of coefficients for a system of linear equations is a symmetric matrix, the problem of determining the inverse for that matrix may be efficiently solved by the use of *Cholesky's method*. This method is exceedingly important since the method of least squares, which we shall meet in the next chapter, involves the solution of a system of linear equations whose coefficient matrix is symmetric.

    In order to illustrate Cholesky's method, consider a symmetric matrix of order 3 by 3:

$$A = \begin{pmatrix} a_{11} & a_{12} & a_{13} \\ a_{21} & a_{22} & a_{23} \\ a_{31} & a_{32} & a_{33} \end{pmatrix}.$$ **5.45**

We now choose to represent A as the product of an upper triangular matrix

$$B = \begin{pmatrix} b_{11} & b_{12} & b_{13} \\ 0 & b_{22} & b_{23} \\ 0 & 0 & b_{33} \end{pmatrix}$$ 5.46

and its transpose B'. That is, let

$$A = B'B,$$ 5.47

or

$$\begin{pmatrix} a_{11} & a_{12} & a_{13} \\ a_{12} & a_{22} & a_{23} \\ a_{13} & a_{23} & a_{33} \end{pmatrix} = \begin{pmatrix} b_{11} & 0 & 0 \\ b_{12} & b_{22} & 0 \\ b_{13} & b_{23} & b_{33} \end{pmatrix} \begin{pmatrix} b_{11} & b_{12} & b_{13} \\ 0 & b_{22} & b_{23} \\ 0 & 0 & b_{33} \end{pmatrix}.$$ 5.48

In expanded form, equation (5.48) becomes

$$\begin{pmatrix} a_{11} & a_{12} & a_{13} \\ a_{12} & a_{22} & a_{23} \\ a_{13} & a_{23} & a_{33} \end{pmatrix} = \begin{pmatrix} b_{11}^2 & b_{11}b_{12} & b_{11}b_{13} \\ b_{11}b_{12} & b_{12}^2 + b_{22}^2 & b_{12}b_{13} + b_{22}b_{23} \\ b_{11}b_{13} & b_{12}b_{13} + b_{22}b_{23} & b_{13}^2 + b_{23}^2 + b_{33}^2 \end{pmatrix}.$$ 5.49

From the definition of the equality of matrices, we may easily solve for the elements of B. Note that some elements of B may be complex numbers. In the case of a general symmetric matrix of order n by n, the following formulas become useful for the computation of the elements of B:

$$b_{11} = \sqrt{a_{11}}; \qquad\qquad b_{1i} = \frac{a_{1i}}{b_{11}};$$

$$b_{22} = \sqrt{a_{22} - b_{12}^2}; \qquad\qquad b_{2i} = \frac{a_{2i} - b_{12}b_{1i}}{b_{22}};$$

$$b_{33} = \sqrt{a_{33} - b_{13}^2 - b_{23}^2}; \qquad b_{3i} = \frac{a_{3i} - b_{13}b_{1i} - b_{23}b_{2i}}{b_{33}};$$ 5.50

$$\cdots$$

$$b_{kk} = \sqrt{a_{kk} - \sum_{j=1}^{k-1} b_{jk}^2}; \qquad b_{ki} = \frac{a_{ki} - \sum_{j=1}^{k-1} b_{jk}b_{ji}}{b_{kk}} \quad \text{for } k < i.$$

These formulas lend themselves readily to use with desk calculators as well as large-scale digital computers.

Now, since $A = B'B$, a system of linear equations of the form

$$AX = C$$ 5.51

may be solved by solving two triangular systems

$$B'Y = C,$$ 5.52

and

$$BX = Y.$$ 5.53

It is obvious that the inverse of an upper (lower) triangular matrix is also an upper (lower) triangular matrix. Hence, B^{-1} may be found by considering the equation

$$\begin{pmatrix} b_{11} & b_{12} & b_{13} \\ 0 & b_{22} & b_{23} \\ 0 & 0 & b_{33} \end{pmatrix} \begin{pmatrix} c_{11} & c_{12} & c_{13} \\ 0 & c_{22} & c_{23} \\ 0 & 0 & c_{33} \end{pmatrix} = \begin{pmatrix} 1 & 0 & 0 \\ 0 & 1 & 0 \\ 0 & 0 & 1 \end{pmatrix}. \qquad \textbf{5.54}$$

Since $(B')^{-1} = (B^{-1})'$, the solution of equation (5.54) yields the necessary information to solve both triangular systems (5.52) and (5.53). In fact, from equations (5.47) and (5.54), it follows that

$$A^{-1} = \begin{pmatrix} c_{11} & c_{12} & c_{13} \\ 0 & c_{22} & c_{23} \\ 0 & 0 & c_{33} \end{pmatrix} \begin{pmatrix} c_{11} & 0 & 0 \\ c_{12} & c_{22} & 0 \\ c_{13} & c_{23} & c_{33} \end{pmatrix}. \qquad \textbf{5.55}$$

EXAMPLE. Determine the solution set to the following system of linear equations:

$$\begin{cases} x_1 - 2x_2 - x_3 = 2, \\ -2x_1 + 5x_2 + 3x_3 = -3, \\ -x_1 + 3x_2 + 6x_3 = 11. \end{cases}$$

Solution: The matrix form of this linear system is

$$\begin{pmatrix} 1 & -2 & -1 \\ -2 & 5 & 3 \\ -1 & 3 & 6 \end{pmatrix} \begin{pmatrix} x_1 \\ x_2 \\ x_3 \end{pmatrix} = \begin{pmatrix} 2 \\ -3 \\ 11 \end{pmatrix}.$$

According to equation (5.48), we set the symmetric coefficient matrix equal to the product of an upper triangular matrix B and its transpose B'. Employing the formulas of (5.50), we have

$$b_{11} = 1, \qquad b_{12} = -2, \qquad b_{13} = -1,$$
$$b_{22} = 1, \qquad b_{23} = 1,$$
$$b_{33} = 2.$$

Our two triangular systems become

$$\begin{pmatrix} 1 & 0 & 0 \\ -2 & 1 & 0 \\ -1 & 1 & 2 \end{pmatrix} \begin{pmatrix} y_1 \\ y_2 \\ y_3 \end{pmatrix} = \begin{pmatrix} 2 \\ -3 \\ 11 \end{pmatrix}$$

and

$$\begin{pmatrix} 1 & -2 & -1 \\ 0 & 1 & 1 \\ 0 & 0 & 2 \end{pmatrix} \begin{pmatrix} x_1 \\ x_2 \\ x_3 \end{pmatrix} = \begin{pmatrix} y_1 \\ y_2 \\ y_3 \end{pmatrix}.$$

Now,

$$\begin{pmatrix} 1 & 0 & 0 \\ -2 & 1 & 0 \\ -1 & 1 & 2 \end{pmatrix}^{-1} = \begin{pmatrix} 1 & 0 & 0 \\ 2 & 1 & 0 \\ -\frac{1}{2} & -\frac{1}{2} & \frac{1}{2} \end{pmatrix}$$

and

$$\begin{pmatrix} 1 & -2 & -1 \\ 0 & 1 & 1 \\ 0 & 0 & 2 \end{pmatrix}^{-1} = \begin{pmatrix} 1 & 2 & -\frac{1}{2} \\ 0 & 1 & -\frac{1}{2} \\ 0 & 0 & \frac{1}{2} \end{pmatrix}.$$

Hence,

$$\begin{pmatrix} y_1 \\ y_2 \\ y_3 \end{pmatrix} = \begin{pmatrix} 1 & 0 & 0 \\ 2 & 1 & 0 \\ -\frac{1}{2} & -\frac{1}{2} & \frac{1}{2} \end{pmatrix} \begin{pmatrix} 2 \\ -3 \\ 11 \end{pmatrix} = \begin{pmatrix} 2 \\ 1 \\ 6 \end{pmatrix}$$

and

$$\begin{pmatrix} x_1 \\ x_2 \\ x_3 \end{pmatrix} = \begin{pmatrix} 1 & 2 & -\frac{1}{2} \\ 0 & 1 & -\frac{1}{2} \\ 0 & 0 & \frac{1}{2} \end{pmatrix} \begin{pmatrix} 2 \\ 1 \\ 6 \end{pmatrix} = \begin{pmatrix} 1 \\ -2 \\ 3 \end{pmatrix}.$$

8. THE METHOD OF RELAXATION

The methods employed thus far in the solution of a system of linear equations are examples of what are termed *direct methods*. Direct methods describe finite sequences of operations which result in exact solutions, save for rounding errors. All direct methods are essentially the same. The methods may differ in the number of operations, the nature of the operations, the order of the operations, or some combination of these.

    A second group of methods for the solution of a system of linear equations are the *iterative methods*. Iterative methods describe a rule for handling an approximation to the solution set which will yield a sequence of improved approximations that will converge to the desired solution set. Generally speaking, the use of an iterative method avoids the problem of rounding errors. However, the slowness of convergence may pose a problem. Hence, many iterative schemes have been and are being developed which converge rapidly when applied to certain types of linear systems.

Many systems of linear equations have diagonal elements whose magnitudes are relatively greater than the magnitudes of the other elements. That is, in the system of equations represented by (5.1), the elements a_{ij} where $i = j$ are relatively greater than those elements a_{ij} where $i \neq j$. One important iterative method which is applicable to this type of linear system is the *method of relaxation*. Under this method, the more dominant the diagonal elements, the more rapid the process of convergence. We shall now illustrate the method of relaxation.

Consider a system of linear equations such as in (5.1) with dominant diagonal elements. Dividing each term of the ith equation by $-a_{ii}$, we obtain the system

$$\begin{cases} -x_1 + b_{12}x_2 + b_{13}x_3 + \cdots + b_{1n}x_n + d_1 = 0, \\ b_{21}x_1 - x_2 + b_{23}x_3 + \cdots + b_{2n}x_n + d_2 = 0, \\ \cdots \\ b_{n1}x_1 + b_{n2}x_2 + b_{n3}x_3 + \cdots - x_n + d_n = 0, \end{cases} \qquad \textbf{5.56}$$

where $b_{ij} = -\dfrac{a_{ij}}{a_{ii}}$ and $d_i = \dfrac{c_i}{a_{ii}}$. At this point one chooses an approximation $({}_1x_1, {}_1x_2, \ldots, {}_1x_n)$ to the solution set. The notation ${}_ix_j$ shall denote the ith approximation to the jth unknown. Substituting our approximation in the linear expressions of (5.56), we obtain

$$\begin{cases} -{}_1x_1 + b_{12}\,{}_1x_2 + b_{13}\,{}_1x_3 + \cdots + b_{1n}\,{}_1x_n + d_1 = R_1, \\ b_{21}\,{}_1x_1 - {}_1x_2 + b_{23}\,{}_1x_3 + \cdots + b_{2n}\,{}_1x_n + d_2 = R_2, \\ \cdots \\ b_{n1}\,{}_1x_1 + b_{n2}\,{}_1x_2 + b_{n3}\,{}_1x_3 + \cdots - {}_1x_n + d_n = R_n. \end{cases}$$

The method of relaxation consists in changing the initial values of the unknowns until all the *residuals* R_i vanish or become negligible. One procedure is to eliminate the largest residual at each step, say R_k, by changing x_k by an amount R_k. With such a change of value of x_k, every R_i is changed by an amount $b_{ik}R_k$. The values of the unknowns and the residuals may be conveniently represented in tabular form as illustrated in the following example:

Consider the linear system

$$\begin{cases} 2x_1 - x_2 - x_3 = 1, \\ x_1 - 4x_2 - 2x_3 = -5, \\ -2x_1 + x_2 - 10x_3 = 10. \end{cases}$$

The system prepared for relaxation appears as

$$\begin{cases} -1.00x_1 + 0.50x_2 + 0.50x_3 + 0.50 = 0, \\ 0.25x_1 - 1.00x_2 - 0.50x_3 + 1.25 = 0, \\ -0.20x_1 + 0.10x_2 - 1.00x_3 - 1.00 = 0. \end{cases}$$

We shall choose $(0, 0, 0)$ as our approximation to the solution set (x_1, x_2, x_3).

TABLE 5.1

x_1	R_1	x_2	R_2	x_3	R_3
0	0.50	0	1.25	0	−1.00
	0.63	1.25	−1.25		0.13
	1.13		0		−0.87
1.13	−1.13		0.28		−0.23
	0		0.28		−1.10
	−0.55		0.55	−1.10	1.10
	−0.55		0.83		0
	0.42	0.83	−0.83		0.08
	−0.13		0		0.08
−0.13	0.13		−0.03		0.03
	0		−0.03		0.11
	0.06		−0.06	0.11	−0.11
	0.06		−0.09		0
	−0.05	−0.09	0.09		−0.01
	0.01		0		−0.01
0.01	−0.01		0		0
	0		0		−0.01
	−0.01		0.01	−0.01	0.01
	−0.01		0.01		0
	0.01	0.01	−0.01		0
	0		0		0

Our approximation and the associated residuals appear in row one of Table 5.1. Since $R_2 = 1.25$ represents the largest residual, x_2 is changed by 1.25. The change of x_2 and the associated changes of the residuals appear in row two under the appropriate columns. The new residuals $R_1 = 1.13$, $R_2 = 0$, and $R_3 = -0.87$ appear in row three. Since $R_1 = 1.13$ now represents the largest residual, x_1 is changed by the amount 1.13 and is noted in row four along with the changes in the residuals. Again, the new residuals appear in the next row, row five. At this point, $R_3 = -1.10$ represents in magnitude the largest residual. Hence, we change x_3 by −1.10 as indicated in row six along with the changes in R_1, R_2, and R_3. The process is continued in the above fashion until the residuals vanish or become negligible. Since the tabular entries in the x_i column represent the starting value of x_i and the changes in x_i, the column sum represents the value of x_i.

Hence,

$$x_1 = 0 + 1.13 - 0.13 + 0.01 = 1.01,$$
$$x_2 = 0 + 1.25 + 0.83 - 0.09 + 0.01 = 2.00,$$

and

$$x_3 = 0 - 1.10 + 0.11 - 0.01 = -1.00.$$

The exact solution set is

$$x_1 = 1, \qquad x_2 = 2, \qquad \text{and} \qquad x_3 = -1.$$

EXERCISES

1. Solve the following systems of linear equations by Cholesky's method:

(a) $\begin{cases} 4x_1 + 2x_2 + 3x_3 = 3, \\ 2x_1 - x_2 + x_3 = -5, \\ 3x_1 + x_2 + 2x_3 = 0; \end{cases}$ (b) $\begin{cases} x_1 - x_2 + x_3 = 11, \\ -x_1 + x_2 + x_3 = 5, \\ x_1 + x_2 + x_3 = 17; \end{cases}$

(c) $\begin{cases} 2x_1 - x_2 + 4x_3 + x_4 = 8, \\ -x_1 + x_2 + 2x_3 + 3x_4 = 17, \\ 4x_1 + 2x_2 + 3x_3 - x_4 = 17, \\ x_1 + 3x_2 - x_3 + 4x_4 = 26; \end{cases}$ (d) $\begin{cases} 3x_1 + 5x_3 = 4, \\ 7x_2 + 4x_3 = 1, \\ 5x_1 + 4x_2 = -14; \end{cases}$

(e) $\begin{cases} x_1 + 2x_2 + 3x_3 = 14, \\ 2x_1 + 3x_2 + 4x_3 = 20, \\ 3x_1 + 4x_2 + 4x_3 = 23. \end{cases}$

2. Solve the following systems of linear equations by the method of relaxation:

(a) $\begin{cases} 8x_1 - 6x_2 + 2x_3 = 27, \\ 2x_1 + 8x_2 + 4x_3 = 44, \\ 5x_1 - 4x_2 - 8x_3 = -7; \end{cases}$ (b) $\begin{cases} -x_1 + 0.4x_2 - 0.3x_3 + 0.2x_4 = 0.5, \\ 0.5x_1 - x_2 - 0.3x_3 + 0.6x_4 = -3.1, \\ 0.4x_1 - 0.3x_2 - x_3 + 0.4x_4 = 0.7, \\ 0.2x_1 + 0.2x_2 + 0.3x_3 - x_4 = 0.1; \end{cases}$

(c) $\begin{cases} 4x_1 + x_2 - x_3 = 40, \\ -x_1 - 2x_2 + x_3 = 14, \\ x_1 + 4x_2 + 6x_3 = 55; \end{cases}$ (d) $\begin{cases} 10x_1 + x_2 - x_3 + 2x_4 = 13, \\ 2x_1 + 10x_2 + 4x_3 + x_4 = 18, \\ x_1 + 4x_2 + 10x_3 - x_4 = -1, \\ x_1 + x_2 - x_3 + 10x_4 = 4. \end{cases}$

6

The Method of Least Squares

I. INTRODUCTION

We have examined in detail the problem of obtaining a polynomial expression which is satisfied by a given set of $n + 1$ points. In many instances, however, it is not desirable to have an approximation function which is satisfied by each of the given points. One reason is that such an approximation function may reflect the random errors of the data. Another reason is that it may be more satisfactory to indicate the general trend of the data, possibly with a smoother, simpler (lower degree) polynomial than we would obtain by one of the standard inter-polation formulas. One criterion under which such an approximation function may be obtained is called the *principle of least squares*. Although the principle of least squares is not limited to the case of fitting a polynomial to a given set of data, we shall be concerned primarily with polynomial approximation functions obtained under this criterion.

2. THE PRINCIPLE OF LEAST SQUARES

If we are given $n + 1$ points $(x_0, y_0), (x_1, y_1), \ldots, (x_n, y_n)$ and it is desired to fit a polynomial of degree $k < n$ to the data, the principle of least squares states that the best representative curve is that for which the sum of the squares of the differences between the y_i's and the $\phi(x_i)$'s of our approximation function is a minimum. That is, it will be necessary to fit a polynomial

$$\phi(x) = a_0 + a_1 x + a_2 x^2 + \cdots + a_k x^k = \sum_{i=0}^{k} a_i x^i \qquad \textbf{6.1}$$

to the data such that

$$\begin{aligned}
&(a_0 + a_1 x_0 + a_2 x_0^2 + \cdots + a_k x_0^k - y_0)^2 \\
&+ (a_0 + a_1 x_1 + a_2 x_1^2 + \cdots + a_k x_1^k - y_1)^2 \\
&+ \cdots + (a_0 + a_1 x_n + a_2 x_n^2 + \cdots + a_k x_n^k - y_n)^2
\end{aligned} \qquad \textbf{6.2}$$

is a minimum. More briefly, we desire to determine the parameters $a_0, a_1, \ldots, a_k$ of the approximation function $\phi(x)$ such that

$$\sum_{i=0}^{n} [\phi(x_i) - y_i]^2 \qquad 6.3$$

will be a minimum. We sometimes write

$$\phi(x_i) - y_i = R_i \qquad 6.4$$

for $i = 0, 1, 2, \ldots, n$, and call these the $n + 1$ *residual equations*.

Now, the residuals R_i will be functions of the coefficients in $\phi(x)$, the a_j's. Furthermore,

$$f(a_0, a_1, \ldots, a_k) = R_0^2 + R_1^2 + R_2^2 + \cdots + R_n^2 = \sum_{i=0}^{n} R_i^2. \qquad 6.5$$

In order for $f(a_0, a_1, \ldots, a_k)$ to be a maximum or a minimum, it can be shown by the methods of the calculus that its partial derivatives with respect to each of the a_j's must be zero. That is,

$$\frac{\partial f}{\partial a_j} = \frac{\partial}{\partial a_j} [R_0^2 + R_1^2 + R_2^2 + \cdots + R_n^2] = 0$$

$$= 2 \left[R_0 \frac{\partial R_0}{\partial a_j} + R_1 \frac{\partial R_1}{\partial a_j} + R_2 \frac{\partial R_2}{\partial a_j} + \cdots + R_n \frac{\partial R_n}{\partial a_j} \right] = 0 \qquad 6.6$$

for $j = 0, 1, 2, \ldots, k$. Now,

$$\frac{\partial R_i}{\partial a_j} = \frac{\partial}{\partial a_j} [\phi(x_i) - y_i]$$

$$= \frac{\partial}{\partial a_j} [a_0 + a_1 x_i + a_2 x_i^2 + \cdots + a_k x_i^k - y_i] \qquad 6.7$$

for $i = 0, 1, 2, \ldots, n$ and $j = 0, 1, 2, \ldots, k$. Then

$$\frac{\partial R_i}{\partial a_0} = 1,$$

$$\frac{\partial R_i}{\partial a_1} = x_i,$$

$$\frac{\partial R_i}{\partial a_2} = x_i^2, \qquad 6.8$$

$$\cdots$$

$$\frac{\partial R_i}{\partial a_k} = x_i^k,$$

for $i = 0, 1, 2, \ldots, n$. The equations of (6.8) may be expressed by the single equation

$$\frac{\partial R_i}{\partial a_j} = x_i^j. \qquad 6.9$$

Hence, the system of equations of partial derivatives of the sum of the squares of the residuals expressed by (6.6) becomes

$$\begin{cases} R_0 + R_1 + R_2 + \cdots + R_n = 0, \\ x_0 R_0 + x_1 R_1 + x_2 R_2 + \cdots + x_n R_n = 0, \\ x_0^2 R_0 + x_1^2 R_1 + x_2^2 R_2 + \cdots + x_n^2 R_n = 0, \\ \cdots \\ x_0^k R_0 + x_1^k R_1 + x_2^k R_2 + \cdots + x_n^k R_n = 0, \end{cases} \qquad \textbf{6.10}$$

by making use of (6.9). Replacing R_i by $\phi(x_i) - y_i$, where $\phi(x_i)$ is defined by (6.1), and collecting the a_j's in each equation, we have

$$\begin{cases} (n + 1)a_0 + \sum x_i a_1 + \sum x_i^2 a_2 + \cdots + \sum x_i^k a_k = \sum y_i, \\ \sum x_i a_0 + \sum x_i^2 a_1 + \sum x_i^3 a_2 + \cdots + \sum x_i^{k+1} a_k = \sum x_i y_i, \\ \sum x_i^2 a_0 + \sum x_i^3 a_1 + \sum x_i^4 a_2 + \cdots + \sum x_i^{k+2} a_k = \sum x_i^2 y_i, \\ \cdots \\ \sum x_i^k a_0 + \sum x_i^{k+1} a_1 + \sum x_i^{k+2} a_2 + \cdots + \sum x_i^{2k} a_k = \sum x_i^k y_i. \end{cases} \qquad \textbf{6.11}$$

All the summations are over i from 0 to n. This system of $k + 1$ equations in the $k + 1$ unknowns, $a_0, a_1, \ldots, a_k$, is called the *system of normal equations*. These equations are solved by the ordinary methods for solving simultaneous equations.

Note that the number of residual equations is equal to the number of given sets of values (x_i, y_i), while the number of normal equations is equal to one more than the degree of the least squares polynomial function $\phi(x)$. It should be mentioned that, in general, the approximation function will not be satisfied by any of the $n + 1$ given points.

That the normal equations determine the a_i's such that $\sum\limits_{i=0}^{n} R_i^2$ is a minimum and not a maximum is obvious since a maximum does not exist. In order to set up the normal equations, one must first compute

$$\sum x_i, \sum x_i^2, \ldots, \sum x_i^{2k}, \sum y_i, \sum x_i y_i, \sum x_i^2 y_i, \ldots, \sum x_i^k y_i.$$

EXAMPLE 1.   By the method of least squares, find the second degree polynomial which best fits the following data:

x	-1	0	1	3	5
y	6	3	4	18	48

Solution: According to (6.11), the form of the normal equations for a second degree least squares interpolation polynomial, $\phi(x) = a_0 + a_1 x + a_2 x^2$, is given by

$$\begin{cases} (n + 1)a_0 + \sum x a_1 + \sum x^2 a_2 = \sum y, \\ \sum x a_0 + \sum x^2 a_1 + \sum x^3 a_2 = \sum xy, \\ \sum x^2 a_0 + \sum x^3 a_1 + \sum x^4 a_2 = \sum x^2 y. \end{cases}$$

Table A is constructed to facilitate the determination of the various necessary sums.

TABLE A

	x	y	xy	x^2	x^2y	x^3	x^4
	-1	6	-6	1	6	-1	1
	0	3	0	0	0	0	0
	1	4	4	1	4	1	1
	3	18	54	9	162	27	81
	5	48	240	25	1200	125	625
Σ	8	79	292	36	1372	152	708

Now, since the number of given points, $n + 1$, equals 5, the normal equations become

$$\begin{cases} 5a_0 + 8a_1 + 36a_2 = 79, \\ 8a_0 + 36a_1 + 152a_2 = 292, \\ 36a_0 + 152a_1 + 708a_2 = 1372. \end{cases}$$

Solving this system of linear equations, we obtain

$$a_0 = 3, \qquad a_1 = -1, \qquad \text{and} \qquad a_2 = 2.$$

Hence, the second degree interpolation polynomial which best fits the data under the least squares criterion is

$$\phi(x) = 3 - x + 2x^2.$$

EXAMPLE 2. Find the linear function, $\phi(x) = a_0 + a_1x$, which best fits the data of Example 1.

Solution: The normal equations are of the form

$$\begin{cases} (n + 1)a_0 + \sum xa_1 = \sum y, \\ \sum xa_0 + \sum x^2a_1 = \sum xy. \end{cases}$$

From the table of Example 1, we have

$$\begin{cases} 5a_0 + 8a_1 = 79, \\ 8a_0 + 36a_1 = 292, \end{cases}$$

or

$$\begin{cases} 5a_0 + 8a_1 = 79, \\ 2a_0 + 9a_1 = 73. \end{cases}$$

By Cramer's Rule,

$$a_0 = \frac{\begin{vmatrix} 79 & 8 \\ 73 & 9 \end{vmatrix}}{\begin{vmatrix} 5 & 8 \\ 2 & 9 \end{vmatrix}} = \frac{127}{29} = 4.4,$$

and

$$a_1 = \frac{\begin{vmatrix} 5 & 79 \\ 2 & 73 \end{vmatrix}}{\begin{vmatrix} 5 & 8 \\ 2 & 9 \end{vmatrix}} = \frac{207}{29} = 7.1.$$

Hence, the best-fitting linear function under the least squares criterion is

$$\phi(x) = 4.4 + 7.1x.$$

EXERCISES

1. Find a linear function which best fits the points $(0, -3)$, $(1, 1)$, $(3, 5)$, $(5, 6)$, and $(6, 11)$.

2. Use the method of least squares to find a second degree polynomial which best fits the following data:

x	0	0.3	0.6	0.9	1.2	1.5
y	3.4	6.1	6.6	8.2	7.9	9.0

3. In an experiment, the distance S(ft.) which a free-falling body traversed at the end of t seconds was observed as follows:

t	0.5	1.0	1.5	2.0	2.5	3.0
S	3.9	16.1	35.8	64.2	99.8	144.0

Find S as the best-fitting second degree polynomial function in t.

4. Find the least squares polynomial of degree three which fits the following data:

x	-2	-1	0	1	2	3
y	-9	-3	1	3	3	1

Discuss the results.

5. Derive formulas for a and b if $y = a + bx$ is the best-fitting linear function for a given set of data.

6. Simplify the formulas of Exercise 5 if **(a)** $\Sigma x = 0$; **(b)** the values of x are $1, 2, \ldots, n$.

7. Show that the best-fitting linear function for the points $(x_1, y_1), (x_2, y_2), \ldots, (x_n, y_n)$ obtained by the method of least squares may be written in the form

$$
\begin{vmatrix}
x & y & 1 \\
\displaystyle\sum_{i=1}^{n} x_i & \displaystyle\sum_{i=1}^{n} y_i & \displaystyle\sum_{i=1}^{n} 1 \\
\displaystyle\sum_{i=1}^{n} x_i^2 & \displaystyle\sum_{i=1}^{n} x_i y_i & \displaystyle\sum_{i=1}^{n} x_i
\end{vmatrix} = 0.
$$

Show that the line passes through the point $(\bar{x}, \bar{y})$, where

$$
\bar{x} = \frac{1}{n} \sum_{i=1}^{n} x_i \quad \text{and} \quad \bar{y} = \frac{1}{n} \sum_{i=1}^{n} y_i.
$$

8. Using the form of Exercise 7, determine the equation of a line which best fits the points $(0, 2)$, $(-1, 0)$, and $(1, 2)$.

9. Show that if $y = a + bx$ is the best-fitting linear function under the least squares criterion for a given set of points $(x_1, y_1), (x_2, y_2), \ldots, (x_n, y_n)$, then

$$
\sum_{i=1}^{n} (y_i - a - bx_i) = 0.
$$

10. Show that the calculation of an arithmetic mean $\bar{y}$ for a given set of values $y_1, y_2, \ldots, y_n$ is equivalent to fitting the line $y = \bar{y}$ to the data under the least squares criterion.

11. Determine a plane $f(x, y) = ax + by + c$ which best fits the points $(1, 0, -4)$, $(1, 1, 0)$, $(-1, 1, 4)$, and $(0, 1, -1)$ under the criterion that

$$
\sum_{i=1}^{4} [f(x_i, y_i) - z_i]^2
$$

be a minimum.

12. Discuss the principle of least squares with an interchange of the roles of x and y. Determine the best-fitting linear function for the data of Exercise 8 with the roles of x and y interchanged.

13. Show that the set of normal equations always has a unique solution for the a_j's.

3. ORTHOGONAL POLYNOMIALS

If the use of a least squares interpolation polynomial of some degree, say k, does not result in yielding sufficient accuracy, a least squares interpolation polynomial of higher degree may be obtained. In order to determine this latter polynomial, an entirely new set of normal equations must be described and solved. This represents a serious disadvantage of the least squares procedure described thus far. Let us, therefore, now discuss another method whereby each coefficient of a least squares interpolation polynomial can be calculated independently, thus allowing for the addition of higher degree terms with a minimum amount of labor. This method, which we shall now discuss, involves the use of *orthogonal polynomials*.

Two polynomials $P(x)$ and $Q(x)$ are said to be *orthogonal* over an interval $a \leq x \leq b$ if

$$\int_a^b P(x) \cdot Q(x) \, dx = 0. \qquad \text{6.12}$$

In terms of equally spaced discrete data, $x = a, a + 1, \ldots, a + n$, two polynomials are said to be *orthogonal* if

$$\sum_{x=a}^{a+n} P(x) \cdot Q(x) = 0. \qquad \text{6.13}$$

A set of polynomials $P_0(x), P_1(x), P_2(x), \ldots, P_k(x)$, with the subscripts indicating the degrees of the polynomials, are said to be *a set of orthogonal polynomials* over the discrete data if

$$\sum_{x=a}^{a+n} P_i(x) \cdot P_j(x) = 0 \qquad \text{for every pair } i, j \text{ where } i \neq j. \qquad \text{6.14}$$

Now, it can be proved that every polynomial in x of degree k can be expressed as a linear function of $k + 1$ orthogonal polynomials in x. That is, if $\phi(x)$ is a kth degree polynomial, then

$$\phi(x) = \alpha_0 P_0(x) + \alpha_1 P_1(x) + \cdots + \alpha_k P_k(x), \qquad \text{6.15}$$

where $P_i(x)$ is an ith degree polynomial and $\Sigma P_i(x) \cdot P_j(x) = 0$ for $i \neq j$ over some specified set of values.

Consider a given set of $n + 1$ equally spaced points $(x_0, y_0), (x_1, y_1), \ldots, (x_n, y_n)$. If we desire to fit to the data a least squares interpolation polynomial of the kth degree, $k \leq n$, we may express that polynomial in the form of (6.15). The coefficients $\alpha_0, \alpha_1, \ldots, \alpha_k$ may be calculated under the least squares criterion that

$$\sum_{i=0}^{n} [\phi(x_i) - y_i]^2$$

be a minimum. The normal equations become

$$\begin{cases} \alpha_0 \sum P_0(x_i) \cdot P_0(x_i) + \alpha_1 \sum P_0(x_i) \cdot P_1(x_i) + \cdots + \alpha_k \sum P_0(x_i) \cdot P_k(x_i) = \sum P_0(x_i) \cdot y_i, \\ \alpha_0 \sum P_1(x_i) \cdot P_0(x_i) + \alpha_1 \sum P_1(x_i) \cdot P_1(x_i) + \cdots + \alpha_k \sum P_1(x_i) \cdot P_k(x_i) = \sum P_1(x_i) \cdot y_i, \\ \cdots \\ \alpha_0 \sum P_k(x_i) \cdot P_0(x_i) + \alpha_1 \sum P_k(x_i) \cdot P_1(x_i) + \cdots + \alpha_k \sum P_k(x_i) \cdot P_k(x_i) = \sum P_k(x_i) \cdot y_i. \end{cases}$$
$$\text{6.16}$$

All the summations are over i from 0 to n. Since

$$\sum_{i=0}^{n} P_r(x_i) \cdot P_s(x_i) = 0$$

for every r, s where $r \neq s$, the normal equations expressed by (6.16) become

$$\begin{cases} \alpha_0 \sum P_0(x_i) \cdot P_0(x_i) = \sum P_0(x_i) \cdot y_i, \\ \alpha_1 \sum P_1(x_i) \cdot P_1(x_i) = \sum P_1(x_i) \cdot y_i, \\ \cdots \\ \alpha_k \sum P_k(x_i) \cdot P_k(x_i) = \sum P_k(x_i) \cdot y_i. \end{cases}$$
$$\text{6.17}$$

It is evident from the equations of (6.17) that the coefficients of the interpolation polynomial of (6.15) may be determined independently.

For a given set of points with $x = 1, 2, \ldots, n$, one set of orthogonal polynomials which may be employed for the above least squares procedure is the set of polynomials:

$$P_0(x) = C_0,$$

$$P_1(x) = C_1(x - \bar{x}),$$

$$P_2(x) = C_2\left[(x - \bar{x})^2 - \frac{(n^2 - 1)}{12}\right],$$

$$P_3(x) = C_3\left[(x - \bar{x})^3 - \frac{(x - \bar{x})(3n^2 - 7)}{20}\right],$$

$$\ldots$$

$$P_{i+1}(x) = C_{i+1}\left[\frac{P_1(x)}{C_1} \cdot \frac{P_i(x)}{C_i} - \frac{i^2(n^2 - i^2)}{4(4i^2 - 1)} \cdot \frac{P_{i-1}(x)}{C_{i-1}}\right],$$

6.18

where $\bar{x}$ is the mean value of the given x's and the C_i's are arbitrary constants which are chosen such that the values of the $P_k(x)$'s are the smallest possible integers for all values of x considered.

Note that a transformation of variables is always possible such that the independent variable becomes x whose values range from 1 to n. Hence, the set of orthogonal polynomials now under examination will be sufficient for least squares problems with equally spaced data.

In order to facilitate the actual determination of the α_i's, tables may be constructed for values of $P_k(x)$ for specified sets of observations. For example, consider a set of observations with $x = 1, 2, \ldots, 7$. Now, employing the equations of (6.18), one set of orthogonal polynomials for $k \leq 4$ over the data is

$$P_0(x) = 1,$$

$$P_1(x) = x - 4,$$

$$P_2(x) = x^2 - 8x + 12,$$

$$P_3(x) = \tfrac{1}{6}(x^3 - 12x^2 + 41x - 36),$$

$$P_4(x) = \tfrac{1}{12}(7x^4 - 112x^3 + 605x^2 - 1256x + 792).$$

6.19

The student should check the derivation of the polynomials of (6.19), noting that $C_0 = C_1 = C_2 = 1$, $C_3 = \tfrac{1}{6}$, and $C_4 = \tfrac{7}{12}$.

The values of these polynomials over the data are shown in Table 6.1. Note that the values of the polynomials of even-degree are symmetric about $\bar{x} = 4$, while the values of the odd-degree polynomials are skew-symmetric about this point. Actually, only a little more than one-half of such tables need be displayed for computational purposes.

TABLE 6.1

x	$P_0(x)$	$P_1(x)$	$P_2(x)$	$P_3(x)$	$P_4(x)$
1	1	-3	5	-1	3
2	1	-2	0	1	-7
3	1	-1	-3	1	1
4	1	0	-4	0	6
5	1	1	-3	-1	1
6	1	2	0	-1	-7
7	1	3	5	1	3

EXAMPLE 1.   Verify that the polynomials of (6.19) are orthogonal over the data.

Solution: If the set of polynomials of (6.19) is to be orthogonal over the data $x = 1, 2, \ldots, 7$, then

$$\sum_{x=1}^{7} P_i(x) \cdot P_j(x) = 0$$

for every pair i, j where $i \neq j$.

Since it is immediately evident from Table 6.1 that

$$\sum_{x=1}^{7} P_0(x) \cdot P_j(x) = \sum_{x=1}^{7} P_j(x) = 0,$$

Table B completes the verification that the polynomials of the set are orthogonal.

TABLE B

x	$P_1(x) \cdot P_2(x)$	$P_1(x) \cdot P_3(x)$	$P_1(x) \cdot P_4(x)$	$P_2(x) \cdot P_3(x)$	$P_2(x) \cdot P_4(x)$	$P_3(x) \cdot P_4(x)$
1	-15	3	-9	-5	15	-3
2	0	-2	14	0	0	-7
3	3	-1	-1	-3	-3	1
4	0	0	0	0	-24	0
5	-3	-1	1	3	-3	-1
6	0	-2	-14	0	0	7
7	15	3	9	5	15	3
Σ	0	0	0	0	0	0

EXAMPLE 2.   Determine both a second degree and a third degree least squares polynomial for the set of points $(1, -12)$, $(2, 2)$, $(3, 11)$, $(4, 20)$, $(5, 20)$, $(6, 16)$, and $(7, 13)$.

Solution: The set of orthogonal polynomials of (6.19) may be employed since the number of points is seven, the data is equally spaced with regard to the independent variable, and the initial value of the independent variable is one.

Now, we first wish to determine an interpolation polynomial $\phi(x)$ of the second degree in the form

$$\phi(x) = \alpha_0 P_0(x) + \alpha_1 P_1(x) + \alpha_2 P_2(x),$$

where

$$P_0(x) = 1,$$

$$P_1(x) = x - 4,$$

and

$$P_2(x) = x^2 - 8x + 12.$$

Making use of the information of Table 6.1, Table C is constructed for the evaluation of the α_k's.

TABLE C

x	y	$P_0(x) \cdot y$	$P_1(x) \cdot y$	$P_2(x) \cdot y$	$P_0(x)^2$	$P_1(x)^2$	$P_2(x)^2$
1	−12	−12	36	−60	1	9	25
2	2	2	−4	0	1	4	0
3	11	11	−11	−33	1	1	9
4	20	20	0	−80	1	0	16
5	20	20	20	−60	1	1	9
6	16	16	32	0	1	4	0
7	13	13	39	65	1	9	25
Σ		70	112	−168	7	28	84

From the equations of (6.17),

$$\alpha_0 = \frac{\sum P_0(x) \cdot y}{\sum P_0(x) \cdot P_0(x)} = \frac{70}{7} = 10,$$

$$\alpha_1 = \frac{\sum P_1(x) \cdot y}{\sum P_1(x) \cdot P_1(x)} = \frac{112}{28} = 4,$$

and

$$\alpha_2 = \frac{\sum P_2(x) \cdot y}{\sum P_2(x) \cdot P_2(x)} = \frac{-168}{84} = -2.$$

Hence,

$$\phi(x) = 10 + 4(x - 4) - 2(x^2 - 8x + 12)$$

$$= 10 + 4x - 16 - 2x^2 + 16x - 24$$

$$= -2x^2 + 20x - 30.$$

The third degree polynomial which best fits the data under the least squares criterion may be expressed as

$$\phi(x) = -2x^2 + 20x - 30 + \alpha_3 P_3(x),$$

where

$$P_3(x) = \tfrac{1}{6}(x^3 - 12x^2 + 41x - 36)$$

and

$$\alpha_3 = \frac{\sum P_3(x) \cdot y}{\sum P_3(x) \cdot P_3(x)}.$$

Again, employing the information of Table 6.1, we have

$$\sum P_3(x) \cdot y = (-1)(-12) + (1)(2) + (1)(11) + (0)(20) + (-1)(20)$$
$$+ (-1)(16) + (1)(13)$$
$$= 2,$$

and

$$\sum P_3(x) \cdot P_3(x) = (-1)^2 + (1)^2 + (1)^2 + (0)^2 + (-1)^2 + (-1)^2 + (1)^2$$
$$= 6.$$

Therefore,
$$\alpha_3 = \tfrac{1}{3}.$$

Hence,

$$\phi(x) = -2x^2 + 20x - 30 + \tfrac{1}{3} \cdot \tfrac{1}{6}(x^3 - 12x^2 + 41x - 36)$$
$$= -2x^2 + 20x - 30 + \tfrac{1}{18}x^3 - \tfrac{2}{3}x^2 + \tfrac{41}{18}x - 2$$
$$= \tfrac{1}{18}(x^3 - 48x^2 + 401x - 576).$$

EXERCISES

1. Determine a least squares polynomial of the fourth degree for the data of Example 2.
2. Show that the following polynomials are orthogonal over the continuous interval $0 \le x \le 1$:

$$P_0(x) = 1,$$
$$P_1(x) = 1 - 2x,$$
$$P_2(x) = 1 - 6x + 6x^2,$$
$$P_3(x) = 1 - 12x + 30x^2 - 20x^3.$$

In addition, show that $\displaystyle\int_0^1 P_n(x)^2\, dx = \frac{1}{2n + 1}$ for $n = 0, 1, 2, 3$.

3. Find a set of orthogonal polynomials over a set of observations for which (a) $x = 1, 2, 3$; (b) $x = 1, 2, 3, 4$.
4. Determine least squares polynomials of degrees 0 through 3 for the following data:

x	1	2	3	4
y	4	1	5	8

Calculate the sum of the squares of the residuals for each interpolation polynomial. Discuss the results.

5. Prove the following properties for the polynomials of (6.18):
   (a) $P_{2n}(x) = P_{2n}(-x)$;
   (b) $P_{2n+1}(x) = -P_{2n+1}(-x)$.

4. POWER FUNCTIONS AND EXPONENTIAL FUNCTIONS

It has been mentioned that the method of least squares is also applicable to the problem of approximating a given set of data by functions other than polynomials. One such type of function which appears frequently in the study of physical systems is the basic *power function*

$$y = cx^n, \qquad 6.20$$

where c and n are constants. The problem of determining a power function which best fits a given set of data (x_0, y_0), (x_1, y_1), $\ldots$, (x_n, y_n) may be approached by the method of least squares after a suitable transformation of variables.

For example, if we take the logarithm of each side of equation (6.20), we obtain

$$\log y = \log c + n \log x. \qquad 6.21$$

Letting $Y = \log y$, $X = \log x$, and $m = \log c$, equation (6.21) becomes linear in X and Y. That is,

$$Y = m + nX. \qquad 6.22$$

By the method of least squares, we may evaluate m and n to determine the best-fitting linear function for the data

$$(\log x_0, \log y_0), (\log x_1, \log y_1), \ldots, (\log x_n, \log y_n).$$

The original parameter n will then be known, and c can be determined from the equation $m = \log c$.

EXAMPLE 1.   Find the power function $y = cx^n$ which best fits the following data under the least squares criterion:

x	2	4	5	6	8
y	0.7500	0.1875	0.1200	0.0833	0.0469

Solution: Letting $X = \log x$ and $Y = \log y$, the given data become

X	0.30103	0.60206	0.69897	0.77815	0.90309
Y	−0.12494	−0.72700	−0.92082	−1.07935	−1.32883

In order to determine the parameters m and n such that the linear function $Y = m + nX$ is the best fit under the least squares criterion, we need to solve the normal equations

$$\begin{cases} 5m + n \sum X = \sum Y, \\ m \sum X + n \sum X^2 = \sum XY. \end{cases}$$

Table D is constructed.

TABLE D

X	Y	X^2	XY
0.30103	−0.12494	0.09062	−0.03761
0.60206	−0.72700	0.36248	−0.43770
0.69897	−0.92082	0.48856	−0.64363
0.77815	−1.07935	0.60552	−0.83990
0.90309	−1.32883	0.81558	−1.20005
$\sum X = 3.28330$	$\sum Y = -4.18094$	$\sum X^2 = 2.36276$	$\sum XY = -3.15889$

Substituting for $\sum X$, $\sum Y$, $\sum X^2$, and $\sum XY$, the normal equations become

$$\begin{cases} 5m + 3.28330n = -4.18094, \\ 3.28330m + 2.36276n = -3.15889. \end{cases}$$

Solving these equations simultaneously, we have

$$\begin{cases} m = 0.47693, \\ n = -1.99969. \end{cases}$$

Now, since $m = \log c$,

$$c = 2.999.$$

Hence, the power function $y = cx^n$ which best fits the given data is

$$y = 3x^{-2}.$$

A second type of function of fairly frequent occurrence in applied problems is the *exponential function*

$$y = ae^{bx}, \qquad \textbf{6.23}$$

where a and b are constants to be determined from the given data. A transformation of variables similar to that employed in handling the power function problem is useful. Taking the natural logarithm of each side of equation (6.23), we have

$$\ln y = \ln a + bx. \qquad \textbf{6.24}$$

Letting $Y = \ln y$, $c = \ln a$, and $X = x$, equation (6.24) becomes

$$Y = c + bX, \qquad\qquad\qquad 6.25$$

which is linear in X and Y. The parameters c and b may be determined to obtain a least squares polynomial of the first degree fitting the data

$$(x_0, \ln y_0), (x_1, \ln y_1), \ldots, (x_n, \ln y_n).$$

The original parameter b of equation (6.23) is known, and a may be determined from the equation $c = \ln a$.

EXAMPLE 2.   Find the exponential function $y = ae^{bx}$ which best fits the following data under the least squares criterion:

x	-4	-2	0	1	2	4
y	0.57	1.32	4.12	6.65	11.0	30.3

Solution: Letting $X = x$ and $Y = \ln y$, the given data become

X	-4	-2	0	1	2	4
Y	-0.56212	0.27763	1.41585	1.89462	2.39790	3.41115

The linear function $Y = c + bX$ of (6.25) which best fits the transformed data under the least squares criterion may be determined by solving the normal equations

$$\begin{cases} 6c + b \sum X = \sum Y, \\ c \sum X + b \sum X^2 = \sum XY. \end{cases}$$

Table E is constructed.

TABLE E

X	Y	X^2	XY
-4	-0.56212	16	2.24848
-2	0.27763	4	-0.55526
0	1.41585	0	0.00000
1	1.89462	1	1.89462
2	2.39790	4	4.79580
4	3.41115	16	13.64460
$\sum X = 1$	$\sum Y = 8.83503$	$\sum X^2 = 41$	$\sum XY = 22.02824$

Substituting for ΣX, ΣY, ΣX^2, and ΣXY, the normal equations become

$$\begin{cases} 6c + b = 8.83503, \\ c + 41b = 22.02824. \end{cases}$$

Solving simultaneously, we have

$$\begin{cases} c = 1.38860, \\ b = 0.50341. \end{cases}$$

Now, since $c = \ln a$,

$$a = 4.01.$$

Hence, the exponential function $y = ae^{bx}$ which best fits the given data is

$$y = 4.01e^{0.50341x}.$$

It should be mentioned that the decision to fit a power function or an exponential function to a given set of data, instead of a polynomial function, is usually arrived at after a plot of the data. Note that points (x, y) satisfying the power function of (6.20) lie along a straight line when plotted on logarithmic paper. Points satisfying the exponential function of (6.23) lie along a straight line when plotted on semilogarithmic paper. Hence, if a plot of points is nearly a straight line on logarithmic or semilogarithmic paper, one would choose a power function or an exponential function, respectively, to fit the data.

EXERCISES

1. By the method of least squares, fit a function of the form $y = cx^n$ to the data:

x	3.2	4.1	5.3	6.0	7.6
y	4.5	7.9	13.1	17.4	31.6

2. The volume of a gas is observed to vary with pressure as follows:

p (gm/cm²)	6.7	9.2	11.3	11.6
v (cc)	1.8	1.3	1.1	1.0

Express p as a power function of v.

3. By the method of least squares, fit a function of the form $y = ae^{bx}$ to the data:

x	0	1	2	3
y	3	8	23	62

4. The number of bacteria in a culture medium is known to be an exponential function of time. The following data were obtained in an experiment:

t(hrs.)	0	1	2	3
$n(10^3/\text{cc})$	1	4	14	41

Determine an interpolation formula.

5. If two variables x and y are known to be related by an equation of the form $y = \dfrac{1}{a + bx}$, what transformation of variables would be necessary in order that data for these variables may be treated by the method of least squares?

6. Fit a curve of the form $y = \dfrac{1}{a + bx}$ to the data:

x	1	2	3	4	5
y	0.42	0.30	0.30	0.24	0.20

5. THE GENERALIZED PROBLEM OF LEAST SQUARES

In the process of determining an interpolation function for a given set of data under the least squares criterion, we have assumed or accepted the independent variable as exact and not subject to error or variation. The assumption of lack of error or variation in one variable is a reasonable one in many cases since it is usually possible to control one of two variables more accurately than the other. However, if we allow both variables to reflect error or variation, the problem of determining the best-fitting function for a given set of data becomes more complicated. We shall now consider this more generalized least squares problem for the determination of a linear interpolation function.

Consider a set of n points $(x_1, y_1), (x_2, y_2), \ldots, (x_n, y_n)$. The *generalized linear interpolation function* for the data is the line

$$ax + by + 1 = 0, \qquad\qquad \textbf{6.26}$$

such that the sum of the squares of the perpendicular distances from the given points to it is a minimum. The perpendicular distance d_i from a point (x_i, y_i) to the line of (6.26) is given by

$$d_i = \frac{|ax_i + by_i + 1|}{\sqrt{a^2 + b^2}}. \qquad\qquad \textbf{6.27}$$

Therefore, we desire to determine the parameters a and b of (6.26) such that $\sum_{i=1}^{n} d_i^2$ is a minimum. Now,

$$\sum_{i=1}^{n} d_i^2 = f(a, b) = \frac{1}{a^2 + b^2} \sum_{i=1}^{n} (ax_i + by_i + 1)^2. \qquad 6.28$$

Taking the partial derivative of $f(a, b)$ with respect to a, we have

$$\frac{\partial f}{\partial a} = \frac{2}{a^2 + b^2} \sum_{i=1}^{n} x_i(ax_i + by_i + 1) - \frac{2a}{(a^2 + b^2)^2} \sum_{i=1}^{n} (ax_i + by_i + 1)^2,$$

or

$$\frac{\partial f}{\partial a} = \frac{2}{(a^2 + b^2)^2}\left[(a^2 + b^2) \sum_{i=1}^{n} x_i(ax_i + by_i + 1) - a \sum_{i=1}^{n} (ax_i + by_i + 1)^2\right]. \qquad 6.29$$

In a similar fashion,

$$\frac{\partial f}{\partial b} = \frac{2}{(a^2 + b^2)^2}\left[(a^2 + b^2) \sum_{i=1}^{n} y_i(ax_i + by_i + 1) - b \sum_{i=1}^{n} (ax_i + by_i + 1)^2\right]. \qquad 6.30$$

Since $\dfrac{\partial f}{\partial a}$ and $\dfrac{\partial f}{\partial b}$ must both vanish if $\sum_{i=1}^{n} d_i^2$ is to be a minimum, we have

$$\begin{cases} (a^2 + b^2) \sum_{i=1}^{n} x_i(ax_i + by_i + 1) - a \sum_{i=1}^{n} (ax_i + by_i + 1)^2 = 0, \\ (a^2 + b^2) \sum_{i=1}^{n} y_i(ax_i + by_i + 1) - b \sum_{i=1}^{n} (ax_i + by_i + 1)^2 = 0. \end{cases} \qquad 6.31$$

Expanding the terms of both equations of (6.31) and rearranging, we have

$$\begin{cases} b(b^2 - a^2) \sum x_iy_i + (b^2 - a^2) \sum x_i - 2ab \sum y_i + ab^2(\sum x_i^2 - \sum y_i^2) - an = 0, \\ a(a^2 - b^2) \sum x_iy_i + (a^2 - b^2) \sum y_i - 2ab \sum x_i - a^2b(\sum x_i^2 - \sum y_i^2) - bn = 0; \end{cases} \qquad 6.32$$

where the summations are over i from 1 to n. Multiplying the first equation of (6.32) by a, the second equation by b, and adding the results, we obtain

$$a \sum x_i + b \sum y_i + n = 0. \qquad 6.33$$

Equation (6.33) and either of the equations of (6.32) may serve as a system of equations for the determination of the parameters a and b.

EXAMPLE.   Determine a generalized least squares linear function representing the following data:

x	-1	0	1	2
y	0	-1	-2	1

Solution: In order to fit a linear function of the form

$$ax + by + 1 = 0$$

to the data under the generalized least squares criterion, the following sums are
necessary: Σx_i, Σy_i, $\Sigma x_i y_i$, Σx_i^2, and Σy_i^2. Table F is constructed for the evaluation of these sums.

TABLE F

	x	y	xy	x^2	y^2
	-1	0	0	1	0
	0	-1	0	0	1
	1	-2	-2	1	4
	2	1	2	4	1
Σ	2	-2	0	6	6

Now, equation (6.33) becomes

$$2a - 2b + 4 = 0.$$

Hence,

$$a = b - 2.$$

Substituting for a in the first equation of (6.32), we have

$$b^2 - b = 0.$$

Solving for b, we obtain

$$b = 0 \quad \text{or} \quad 1.$$

The corresponding values of a are

$$a = -2 \quad \text{or} \quad -1.$$

Therefore, we have obtained two linear functions:

$$L_1: \quad x = \tfrac{1}{2},$$
$$L_2: \quad y = x - 1.$$

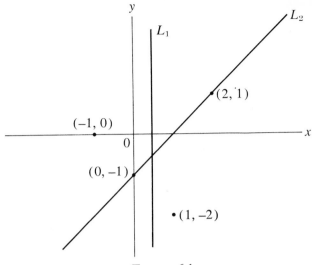

FIGURE 6.1

A graph of these functions with the given points appears in Figure 6.1. It may not be immediately evident which is the best-fitting linear function under the generalized least squares criterion. Now, for the linear function L_1,

$$\sum_{i=1}^{4} d_i^2 = (-1 - \tfrac{1}{2})^2 + (0 - \tfrac{1}{2})^2 + (1 - \tfrac{1}{2})^2 + (2 - \tfrac{1}{2})^2 = 5.$$

For the linear function L_2,

$$\sum_{i=1}^{4} d_i^2 = \tfrac{1}{2}[(2)^2 + 0^2 + (-2)^2 + 0^2] = 4.$$

Hence, the desired linear function is L_2.

Note that the equations of (6.32) indicate that, in general, we may expect three sets of values for the parameters a and b. In such instances, the graphs of the resulting linear functions with the plots of the given data may be helpful in deciding which function is the desired one. In some cases, it may be necessary to calculate $\sum_{i=1}^{n} d_i^2$ for each function.

EXERCISES

1. Determine a generalized least squares linear function representing the following data:

x	−1	0	1	2
y	2	3	7	8

2.   Given the data:

x	−2	2	3	7	9
y	−2	0	3	4	6

Find the best-fitting linear function by:

(a) minimizing the sum of the squares of the vertical distances from the points to the line;

(b) minimizing the sum of the squares of the horizontal distances from the points to the line;

(c) minimizing the sum of the squares of the perpendicular distances from the points to the line.

3.   Show that the generalized least squares linear function for a given set of data is satisfied by the point $(\bar{x}, \bar{y})$ whose coordinates are the arithmetic means of the two variables x and y. That is, $\bar{x} = \dfrac{\Sigma x}{n}$ and $\bar{y} = \dfrac{\Sigma y}{n}$.

4.   It is sometimes desirable to fit a polynomial to a set of points such that the sum of the weighted squares of the residuals is a minimum. That is,

$$\sum_{i=1}^{n} w_i R_i^2$$

is to be minimized, where w_i is the weighting factor associated with the ith residual, R_i. Determine the normal equations in such a case.

5.   Making use of the results of Exercise 4, find the best-fitting least squares polynomial of degree two for the following data with associated weighting factors:

x	−1	0	1	2
y	7	3	5	12
w	2	3	2	1

7

Fourier Series and Harmonic Analysis

I. INTRODUCTION

In elementary calculus, we were concerned with the following type of problem. Given a function of an independent variable, find an infinite series equal to the function in some range of values. For example, in order to find such a series for the natural logarithmic function, we may use a Taylor expansion in terms of powers of $(x - 1)$. The Taylor expansion states that, for any function of x,

$$f(x) = f(a) + f'(a)(x - a) + \frac{f''(a)}{2!}(x - a)^2 + \frac{f'''(a)}{3!}(x - a)^3 + \cdots$$

$$= \sum_{n=0}^{\infty} \frac{f^n(a)}{n!}(x - a)^n.$$

7.1

Here, $a = 1$. Therefore,

$$f(a) = \ln 1 = 0,$$

$$f'(a) = \frac{d \ln x}{dx}\bigg]_{x=1} = \frac{1}{x}\bigg]_{x=1} = 1,$$

$$f''(a) = \frac{d^2 \ln x}{dx^2}\bigg]_{x=1} = -\frac{1}{x^2}\bigg]_{x=1} = -1,$$

$$f'''(a) = \frac{d^3 \ln x}{dx^3}\bigg]_{x=1} = \frac{2}{x^3}\bigg]_{x=1} = 2,$$

$$\cdots$$

Now,

$$\ln x = (x - 1) - \tfrac{1}{2}(x - 1)^2 + \tfrac{1}{3}(x - 1)^3 - \cdots \qquad \text{for } 0 < x \le 2.$$

The function $\ln x$ can now be approximated in the interval $0 < x \le 2$ to any desired degree of accuracy by using a finite number of terms of the infinite series. Certain restrictions were placed upon such an expansion. For example, all the derivatives of $f(x)$ had to exist as finite numbers for $x = a$. Functions

$f(x)$ that are much more general in character than those represented by a Taylor series can be expanded in a *Fourier series*, a series of the form

$$
\begin{aligned}
f(x) &= \tfrac{1}{2}a_0 + a_1 \cos x + a_2 \cos 2x + a_3 \cos 3x + \cdots \\
&\quad + b_1 \sin x + b_2 \sin 2x + b_3 \sin 3x + \cdots \\
&= \tfrac{1}{2}a_0 + (a_1 \cos x + b_1 \sin x) \\
&\quad + (a_2 \cos 2x + b_2 \sin 2x) \\
&\quad + (a_3 \cos 3x + b_3 \sin 3x) + \cdots.
\end{aligned}
\tag{7.2}
$$

That is,

$$
f(x) = \tfrac{1}{2}a_0 + \sum_{n=1}^{\infty} (a_n \cos nx + b_n \sin nx).
\tag{7.3}
$$

2. EULER'S FORMULAS

The process of evaluating the a_n's and b_n's in equation (7.2) is one of integration. We must first verify the evaluation of the following integrals for positive integers m and n:

$$
\int_{-\pi}^{\pi} \sin nx \cos mx \, dx = 0,
\tag{7.4}
$$

$$
\int_{-\pi}^{\pi} \sin nx \sin mx \, dx = \begin{cases} 0, & \text{for } n \neq m, \\ \pi, & \text{for } n = m, \end{cases}
\tag{7.5}
$$

$$
\int_{-\pi}^{\pi} \cos nx \cos mx \, dx = \begin{cases} 0, & \text{for } n \neq m, \\ \pi, & \text{for } n = m. \end{cases}
\tag{7.6}
$$

You will recall from elementary trigonometry that

$$
\sin (A + B) = \sin A \cos B + \cos A \sin B,
$$

$$
\sin (A - B) = \sin A \cos B - \cos A \sin B.
$$

Adding these equations, we have

$$
\sin (A + B) + \sin (A - B) = 2 \sin A \cos B.
$$

After dividing by 2 and letting $A = nx$ and $B = mx$, we have

$$
\tfrac{1}{2} \sin [(n + m)x] + \tfrac{1}{2} \sin [(n - m)x] = \sin nx \cos mx.
$$

Then

$$
\int_{-\pi}^{\pi} \sin nx \cos mx \, dx = \frac{1}{2} \int_{-\pi}^{\pi} [\sin (n + m)x + \sin (n - m)x] \, dx
$$

$$
= \frac{1}{2} \left[-\frac{1}{n + m} \cos (n + m)x - \frac{1}{n - m} \cos (n - m)x \right]_{-\pi}^{\pi}
$$

$$= \frac{1}{2}\left[-\frac{1}{n+m}\cos(n+m)\pi - \frac{1}{n-m}\cos(n-m)\pi \right.$$

$$\left. + \frac{1}{n+m}\cos(n+m)(-\pi) + \frac{1}{n-m}\cos(n-m)(-\pi) \right]$$

$$= 0,$$

since

$$\cos\theta = \cos(-\theta).$$

Equations (7.5) and (7.6) can be verified by similar derivations and we leave these for the student to do.

Now, to evaluate the coefficients of the Fourier series, we multiply both sides of equation (7.2) by $\cos mx\, dx$, where m is a nonnegative integer, and integrate term by term from $x = -\pi$ to $x = \pi$. Hence,

$$\int_{-\pi}^{\pi} f(x)\cos mx\, dx = \frac{a_0}{2}\int_{-\pi}^{\pi} \cos mx\, dx$$

$$+ \sum_{n=1}^{\infty} a_n \int_{-\pi}^{\pi} \cos nx \cos mx\, dx$$

$$+ \sum_{n=1}^{\infty} b_n \int_{-\pi}^{\pi} \sin nx \cos mx\, dx.$$

Making use of equations (7.4), (7.5), and (7.6), the expression reduces to

$$\int_{-\pi}^{\pi} f(x)\cos mx\, dx = \frac{a_0}{2}\int_{-\pi}^{\pi} \cos mx\, dx + \pi a_m, \quad \text{if } m \neq 0.$$

If we let $m = 0$, we have

$$\int_{-\pi}^{\pi} f(x)\, dx = \pi a_0,$$

whereby

$$a_0 = \frac{1}{\pi}\int_{-\pi}^{\pi} f(x)\, dx.$$

For $m = 1, 2, 3, \ldots$, we have

$$a_m = \frac{1}{\pi}\int_{-\pi}^{\pi} f(x)\cos mx\, dx.$$

Since m can be any particular value of n, we have

$$a_n = \frac{1}{\pi}\int_{-\pi}^{\pi} f(x)\cos nx\, dx, \qquad 7.7$$

where n is any nonnegative integer.

The use of $\dfrac{a_0}{2}$ as the constant term enables us to include the formula for a_0 in that for a_n.

By a similar process, we can find b_m after multiplying by sin mx dx instead of cos mx dx. We then obtain

$$b_n = \frac{1}{\pi} \int_{-\pi}^{\pi} f(x) \sin nx \, dx, \qquad \textbf{7.8}$$

where n is any positive integer.

Formulas (7.7) and (7.8) are known as the *Euler formulas* for finding the *Fourier coefficients*. By computing the Fourier coefficients for any given function and substituting in equation (7.2), we obtain the Fourier series expansion for the function.

3. FOURIER'S THEOREM

A function $f(x)$ for which $f(x + k) = f(x)$ is called a *periodic function* of period k.

Theorem. *If $f(x)$ is a periodic bounded function of period 2π and contains at most a finite number of maximum and minimum points and a finite number of discontinuities within each interval, then the Fourier series of $f(x)$ converges to $f(x)$ at all points where $f(x)$ is continuous and converges to the average of the left-hand and right-hand limits of $f(x)$ at each point of discontinuity. Furthermore, the Fourier series of $f(x)$ represents $f(x)$ everywhere. If $f(x)$ is a nonperiodic function satisfying all the other conditions, then the Fourier series of $f(x)$ converges to $f(x)$ at all points within the interval used in calculating the Fourier coefficients.*

This theorem, known as *Fourier's Theorem*, was proved by Dirichlet, a German mathematician, in 1829. The conditions of the theorem are sometimes called the *Dirichlet conditions*, and are the conditions necessary for $f(x)$ to possess a valid Fourier expansion. These conditions are satisfied by almost every conceivable function in engineering applications such as in vibration theory, heat diffusion theory, etc.

EXAMPLE 1.   Find the Fourier series expansion for $f(x) = x^2$ in the interval $x = -\pi$ to $x = \pi$.

Solution: Now, we need to determine the coefficients a_n and b_n in the equation

$$x^2 = \frac{a_0}{2} + \sum_{n=1}^{\infty} (a_n \cos nx + b_n \sin nx).$$

From the Euler formulas,

$$a_0 = \frac{1}{\pi} \int_{-\pi}^{\pi} x^2 \, dx = \frac{2\pi^2}{3},$$

$$a_n = \frac{1}{\pi} \int_{-\pi}^{\pi} x^2 \cos nx \, dx†$$

$$= (-1)^n \frac{4}{n^2} \qquad \text{for } n = 1, 2, 3, \ldots,$$

$$b_n = \frac{1}{\pi} \int_{-\pi}^{\pi} x^2 \sin nx \, dx†$$

$$= 0 \qquad \text{for } n = 1, 2, 3, \ldots.$$

Therefore, the expansion becomes

$$x^2 = \frac{\pi^2}{3} - 4\left(\cos x - \frac{\cos 2x}{2^2} + \frac{\cos 3x}{3^2} - \frac{\cos 4x}{4^2} + \cdots \right).$$

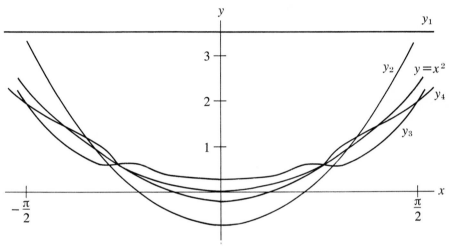

FIGURE 7.1

If on the same graph of $y = x^2$ (Figure 7.1) we sketch the partial sums of the terms of the Fourier series expansion

$$y_1 = \frac{\pi^2}{3},$$

$$y_2 = \frac{\pi^2}{3} - 4 \cos x,$$

$$y_3 = \frac{\pi^2}{3} - 4 \cos x + \cos 2x,$$

and

$$y_4 = \frac{\pi^2}{3} - 4 \cos x + \cos 2x - \frac{4}{9} \cos 3x,$$

we are able to see graphically how the successive partial sums more closely approximate the function x^2 in the interval $-\frac{\pi}{2}$ to $\frac{\pi}{2}$. Since x^2 is not a periodic

† Use integration by parts to evaluate.

function, the Fourier expansion in this example is only valid in the interval $x = -\pi$ to $x = \pi$.

EXAMPLE 2.   A function $f(x)$ is defined as $f(x) = -c$ from $x = -\pi$ to $x = 0$ and $f(x) = c$ from $x = 0$ to $x = \pi$. In addition, $f(x)$ is a periodic function with period 2π. Find its Fourier series (Figure 7.2).

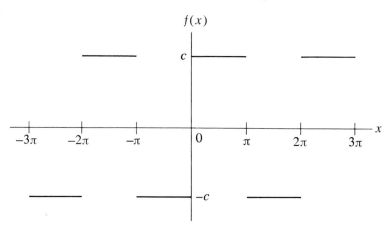

FIGURE 7.2

Solution: Now,

$$a_0 = \frac{1}{\pi} \int_{-\pi}^{0} (-c)\, dx + \frac{1}{\pi} \int_{0}^{\pi} c\, dx = 0,$$

$$a_n = -\frac{c}{\pi} \int_{-\pi}^{0} \cos nx\, dx + \frac{c}{\pi} \int_{0}^{\pi} \cos nx\, dx = 0 \qquad \text{for } n = 1, 2, 3, \ldots,$$

$$b_n = -\frac{c}{\pi} \int_{-\pi}^{0} \sin nx\, dx + \frac{c}{\pi} \int_{0}^{\pi} \sin nx\, dx$$

$$= -\frac{c}{\pi}\left[-\frac{1}{n}\cos nx \right]_{-\pi}^{0} + \frac{c}{\pi}\left[-\frac{1}{n}\cos nx \right]_{0}^{\pi}$$

$$= -\frac{c}{\pi}\left[-\frac{1}{n} + \frac{1}{n}\cos n\pi \right] + \frac{c}{\pi}\left[-\frac{1}{n}\cos n\pi + \frac{1}{n} \right]$$

$$= \frac{2c}{\pi n}\left[1 + (-1)^{n+1} \right] \qquad \text{for } n = 1, 2, 3, \ldots.$$

Therefore,

$$f(x) = \frac{4c}{\pi}\left[\sin x + \frac{\sin 3x}{3} + \frac{\sin 5x}{5} + \cdots \right].$$

The Fourier series represents the function for all values of x since the function is periodic of period 2π. Note also that at a point of discontinuity the series converges to the average of the left-hand and right-hand limits of the function at that point. For example, at $x = \pi$ the Fourier series yields a value of zero.

EXAMPLE 3.   Find the Fourier series for $f(x) = x$ from $-\pi$ to π.

Solution: Now,

$$a_0 = \frac{1}{\pi} \int_{-\pi}^{\pi} x \, dx = 0,$$

$$a_n = \frac{1}{\pi} \int_{-\pi}^{\pi} x \cos nx \, dx = 0 \qquad \text{for } n = 1, 2, 3, \ldots,$$

$$b_n = \frac{1}{\pi} \int_{-\pi}^{\pi} x \sin nx \, dx \qquad \text{for } n = 1, 2, 3, \ldots.$$

Let $u = x$, $dv = \sin nx \, dx$, then $du = dx$, $v = -\dfrac{1}{n} \cos nx$. Then

$$\int_{-\pi}^{\pi} x \sin nx \, dx = \left[-\frac{x}{n} \cos nx \right]_{-\pi}^{\pi} + \frac{1}{n} \int_{-\pi}^{\pi} \cos nx \, dx$$

$$= -\frac{2\pi}{n}(-1)^n + \frac{1}{n^2} [\sin nx]_{-\pi}^{\pi}$$

$$= \frac{2\pi(-1)^{n+1}}{n} \qquad \text{for } n = 1, 2, 3, \ldots.$$

Therefore,

$$x = 2\left(\sin x - \frac{\sin 2x}{2} + \frac{\sin 3x}{3} - \cdots \right)$$

for $-\pi < x < \pi$.

EXERCISES

1. Derive equations (7.5) and (7.6).

2. Derive the Euler formula for b_n, equation (7.8).

3. Derive the Euler formulas for a function $f(x)$ represented in the interval

$$d < x < d + 2\pi.$$

4. Find the Fourier series expansion for $f(x)$ where

$$f(x) = 0 \qquad \text{for } -\pi < x < 0,$$
$$= x^2 \qquad \text{for } 0 < x < \pi.$$

Sketch $f(x)$ and the curve of the first five terms of the Fourier expansion.

Find the Fourier series expansion for the following functions:

5. $f(x) = \pi - 2x \qquad$ for $0 < x < \pi$,

$\qquad = \pi + 2x \qquad$ for $-\pi < x < 0$.

6. $f(x) = \dfrac{x^2}{k} \qquad$ for $-\pi < x < \pi$.

7. $f(x) = 0 \qquad$ for $-\pi < x < 0$,

$\qquad = \sin x \qquad$ for $0 < x < \pi$.

8. $f(x) = e^x \qquad$ for $-\pi < x < \pi$.

9. $f(x) = \dfrac{\sin 2nx}{\sin x} \qquad$ for $-\pi < x < \pi$.

10. $f(x) = |\cos x| \qquad$ for $0 < x < 2\pi$.

4. ODD AND EVEN FUNCTIONS

If a function is to be represented from d to $d + 2\pi$ instead of $-\pi$ to π, it can be shown that the only difference in the formulas for a_n and b_n is in the limits of integration, which now become from d to $d + 2\pi$. Although any interval of length 2π can be used in determining the Fourier series expansion of a periodic function, the interval $-\pi \le x \le \pi$ has certain advantages for the utilization of symmetric properties of functions.

If $f(x) = f(-x)$, then $f(x)$ is said to be an *even function* and has a graph symmetric with respect to the function axis. Examples of even functions include x^2, $|x|$, and $\cos x$.

If $f(x) = -f(-x)$, then $f(x)$ is said to be an *odd function* and has a graph symmetric with respect to the origin of the rectangular coordinate system. Examples of odd functions include x, x^3, and $\sin x$.

The product of an odd function and an even function is an odd function, while the product of two odd functions or two even functions is even. The proof follows immediately from the definitions of odd and even functions.

For example, consider the two functions $f(x)$ and $g(x)$, with their product equal to $h(x)$, that is,

$$f(x) \cdot g(x) = h(x).$$

If $f(x)$ is odd and $g(x)$ is even, then

$$[-f(-x)][g(-x)] = -h(-x) \quad \text{and} \quad h(x) = -h(-x).$$

Hence, $h(x)$ is odd. If $f(x)$ and $g(x)$ are both odd or both even, then

$$[\mp f(-x)][\mp g(-x)] = h(-x) \quad \text{and} \quad h(x) = h(-x).$$

Hence, $h(x)$ is even. Furthermore,

$$\int_{-a}^{a} f(x)\,dx = \begin{cases} 0 & \text{if } f(x) \text{ is odd,} \\ 2\int_{0}^{a} f(x)\,dx & \text{if } f(x) \text{ is even.} \end{cases} \qquad \textbf{7.9}$$

Since cos nx is an even function and sin nx is an odd function for all positive integers n, we see that when $f(x)$ is odd, $f(x)$ cos nx is also odd and $f(x)$ sin nx is even. Hence, the series for an odd function will contain neither cosine terms nor a constant term since

$$a_n = \frac{1}{\pi} \int_{-\pi}^{\pi} f(x) \cos nx\,dx = 0 \qquad \text{for } n = 0, 1, 2, \ldots, \qquad \textbf{7.10}$$

and

$$b_n = \frac{2}{\pi} \int_{0}^{\pi} f(x) \sin nx\,dx \qquad \text{for } n = 1, 2, 3, \ldots. \qquad \textbf{7.11}$$

Similarly, the series for an even function will contain no sine terms since

$$a_n = \frac{2}{\pi} \int_{0}^{\pi} f(x) \cos nx\,dx \qquad \text{for } n = 0, 1, 2, \ldots, \qquad \textbf{7.12}$$

and

$$b_n = \frac{1}{\pi} \int_{-\pi}^{\pi} f(x) \sin nx\,dx = 0 \qquad \text{for } n = 1, 2, 3, \ldots. \qquad \textbf{7.13}$$

EXAMPLE.   If $f(x) = -x$ from $x = -\pi$ to $x = 0$ and $f(x) = x$ from $x = 0$ to $x = \pi$, find its Fourier series valid from $-\pi$ to π.

Solution: Since $f(x)$ is an even function, its Fourier series does not contain any sine terms. Now,

$$a_0 = \frac{2}{\pi} \int_{0}^{\pi} x\,dx = \pi,$$

$$a_n = \frac{2}{\pi} \int_{0}^{\pi} x \cos nx\,dx$$

$$= \frac{2}{\pi}\left[\frac{x}{n} \sin nx\right]_{0}^{\pi} - \frac{2}{\pi n} \int_{0}^{\pi} \sin nx\,dx$$

$$= \frac{2}{\pi n^2} [\cos nx]_{0}^{\pi}$$

$$= \frac{2}{\pi n^2} [\cos n\pi - 1]$$

$$= \frac{2}{\pi n^2} [(-1)^n - 1] \qquad \text{for } n = 1, 2, 3, \ldots.$$

Therefore,

$$f(x) = \frac{\pi}{2} - \frac{4}{\pi}\left(\cos x + \frac{\cos 3x}{9} + \frac{\cos 5x}{25} + \cdots\right).$$

5. HALF-RANGE FOURIER SERIES

We have seen that odd and even functions in the interval $-\pi < x < \pi$ can be expressed in terms of *Fourier sine series* and *Fourier cosine series*, respectively. Now, for both types of functions, the Euler formulas for the Fourier coefficients make use only of the values of $f(x)$ between $x = 0$ and $x = \pi$. Hence, for any function $f(x)$ given only over this interval $0 < x < \pi$, we can form either the Fourier sine or cosine series. The series will converge to $f(x)$ for $0 < x < \pi$ and, outside this interval, to the odd periodic function which coincides with $f(x)$ for $0 < x < \pi$ if it is a Fourier sine series; to the even periodic function which coincides with $f(x)$ for $0 < x < \pi$ if it is a Fourier cosine series.

These two periodic extensions of functions defined between 0 and π are contrasted for the same function in Figures 7.3 and 7.4.

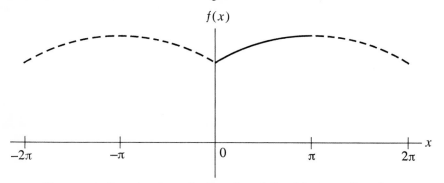

Even periodic extension of a function defined between 0 and π.

FIGURE 7.3

Odd periodic extension of a function defined between 0 and π.

FIGURE 7.4

EXAMPLE.   A function is defined as equal to $\pi - x$ for $0 < x < \pi$. Find its Fourier series valid in the interval defined.

Solution: In this case, the function may be considered an even or odd function and can be represented by a Fourier cosine series or Fourier sine series, respectively.

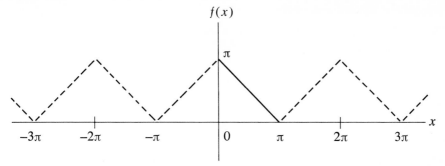

FIGURE 7.5

If we consider $f(x)$ to be an even function, as in Figure 7.5, then

$$a_0 = \frac{2}{\pi} \int_0^{\pi} (\pi - x)\, dx = \frac{2}{\pi}\left[\pi x - \frac{x^2}{2}\right]_0^{\pi} = \pi,$$

$$a_n = \frac{2}{\pi} \int_0^{\pi} (\pi - x) \cos nx\, dx$$

$$= \frac{2}{\pi n^2}[(-1)^{n+1} + 1] \qquad \text{for } n = 1, 2, 3, \ldots,$$

$$b_n = 0 \qquad \text{for } n = 1, 2, 3, \ldots.$$

Therefore,

$$f(x) = \frac{\pi}{2} + \frac{4}{\pi}\left(\cos x + \frac{\cos 3x}{9} + \frac{\cos 5x}{25} + \cdots\right).$$

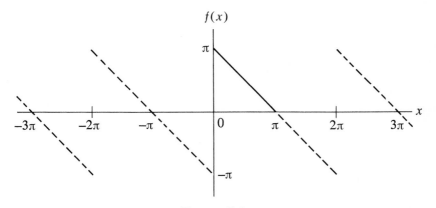

FIGURE 7.6

If we consider $f(x)$ to be an odd function, as in Figure 7.6, then

$$a_n = 0 \qquad \text{for } n = 0, 1, 2, 3, \ldots,$$

$$b_n = \frac{2}{\pi} \int_0^{\pi} (\pi - x) \sin nx\, dx \qquad \text{for } n = 1, 2, 3, \ldots.$$

Integrating by parts, we obtain

$$b_n = \frac{2}{\pi}\left[\frac{(x-\pi)}{n}\cos nx\right]_0^\pi - \frac{2}{\pi n}\int_0^\pi \cos nx \, dx$$

$$= \frac{2}{n} \quad \text{for } n = 1, 2, 3, \ldots.$$

Hence,

$$f(x) = 2\left(\sin x + \frac{\sin 2x}{2} + \frac{\sin 3x}{3} + \cdots\right).$$

EXERCISES

1. Determine whether the following functions are odd or even:

   (a) $x^4 - 3x^2$;   (b) $x^3 + 3x$;

   (c) $x^2 - 4$;   (d) $x \sin x$;

   (e) $x \cos x$;   (f) e^x;

   (g) $\sin^3 x$;   (h) $\cos kx$;

   (i) 3;   (j) $|\sin x|$.

2. Evaluate:

   (a) $\displaystyle\int_{-\pi}^{\pi} x^2 \sin kx \, dx$;

   (b) $\displaystyle\int_{-c}^{c} \cos 3x \sin 5x \, dx$.

3. Making use of the identity

   $$f(x) = \tfrac{1}{2}[f(x) - f(-x)] + \tfrac{1}{2}[f(x) + f(-x)],$$

   show that every function may be expressed as the sum of an odd and even function.

   Find the Fourier series for the following functions:

4.

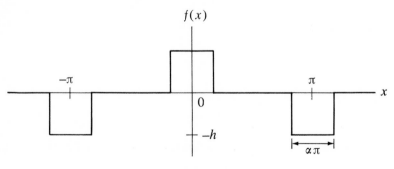

DRAWING 1

5.

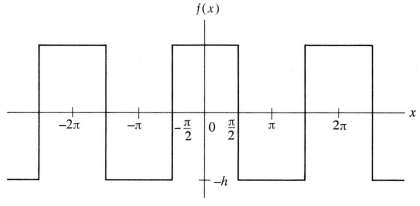

DRAWING 2

6.

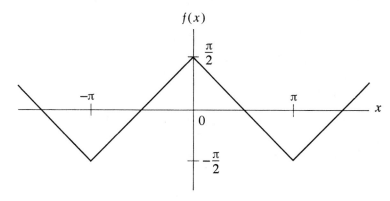

DRAWING 3

7. $f(x) = |\sin x|$.

8. $f(x) = 0$ for $-\pi < x < 0$,
      $= \pi$ for $0 < x < \pi$.

9. $f(x) = \cos kx$ for $-\pi < x < \pi$.

6. CHANGE OF SCALE

By a transformation, or change in variable, we can obtain the Fourier series which represents a function in the interval $-\dfrac{L}{2}$ to $\dfrac{L}{2}$. In addition, if the function has a period of length L, the Fourier series will represent the function everywhere.

If

$$g(y) = \frac{a_0}{2} + \sum_{n=1}^{\infty} (a_n \cos ny + b_n \sin ny),$$

let $y = kx$ where k is determined such that $y = \pi$ when $x = \frac{L}{2}$, or $y = -\pi$ when $x = -\frac{L}{2}$. Furthermore, let $g(y) = f(x)$. Then it follows that

$$f(x) = \frac{a_0}{2} + \sum_{n=1}^{\infty} \left(a_n \cos \frac{2\pi nx}{L} + b_n \sin \frac{2\pi nx}{L} \right), \qquad \textbf{7.14}$$

where

$$a_n = \frac{2}{L} \int_{-L/2}^{L/2} f(x) \cos \frac{2\pi nx}{L} \, dx \qquad \text{for } n = 0, 1, 2, 3, \ldots, \qquad \textbf{7.15}$$

and

$$b_n = \frac{2}{L} \int_{-L/2}^{L/2} f(x) \sin \frac{2\pi nx}{L} \, dx \qquad \text{for } n = 1, 2, 3, \ldots. \qquad \textbf{7.16}$$

Equations (7.15) and (7.16) may be obtained from

$$a_n = \frac{1}{\pi} \int_{-\pi}^{\pi} g(y) \cos ny \, dy$$

and

$$b_n = \frac{1}{\pi} \int_{-\pi}^{\pi} g(y) \sin ny \, dy$$

by a change in variable from y to x where

$$y = \frac{2\pi}{L} x \quad \text{and} \quad dy = \frac{2\pi}{L} \, dx.$$

EXAMPLE 1.   Find the Fourier series for

$$f(x) = -1 \qquad \text{for } -2 \leq x \leq 0,$$
$$= 1 \qquad \text{for } 0 \leq x \leq 2.$$

Solution: Here, $f(x)$ is an odd function. Therefore,

$$a_n = 0 \qquad \text{for } n = 0, 1, 2, \ldots$$

and

$$b_n = \frac{2}{L} \int_{-L/2}^{L/2} f(x) \sin \frac{2\pi nx}{L} \, dx,$$

or

$$b_n = \frac{4}{L} \int_{0}^{L/2} f(x) \sin \frac{2\pi nx}{L} \, dx \qquad \text{for } n = 1, 2, 3, \ldots.$$

Since $L = 4$,

$$b_n = \int_0^2 \sin \frac{\pi n x}{2} \, dx$$

$$= -\frac{2}{\pi n} \left[\cos \frac{\pi n x}{2} \right]_0^2$$

$$= \frac{2}{\pi n} [1 + (-1)^{n+1}] \qquad \text{for } n = 1, 2, 3, \ldots.$$

Therefore,

$$f(x) = \frac{4}{\pi} \left(\sin \frac{\pi}{2} x + \frac{1}{3} \sin \frac{3\pi}{2} x + \frac{1}{5} \sin \frac{5\pi}{2} x + \cdots \right).$$

EXAMPLE 2. Find the Fourier sine series which represents the function shown in Figure 7.7 from 0 to $\frac{\pi}{2}$.

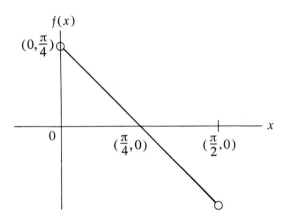

FIGURE 7.7

Solution: Now,

$$f(x) = \frac{\pi}{4} - x \qquad \text{for } 0 < x < \frac{\pi}{2},$$

and $\frac{L}{2} = \frac{\pi}{2}$, or $L = \pi$. To find the Fourier sine series, we may think of $f(x)$ as an odd function in the interval $-\frac{\pi}{2} < x < \frac{\pi}{2}$ although we are only interested in the function in the interval for which it was defined originally. Therefore,

$$a_n = 0 \qquad \text{for } n = 0, 1, 2, \ldots,$$

and

$$b_n = \frac{4}{L} \int_0^{L/2} \left(\frac{\pi}{4} - x\right) \sin \frac{2\pi n x}{L} \, dx$$

$$= \frac{4}{\pi} \int_0^{\pi/2} \left(\frac{\pi}{4} - x\right) \sin 2nx \, dx$$

$$= \frac{4}{\pi}\left[-\frac{1}{2n}\left(\frac{\pi}{4} - x\right) \cos 2nx \right]_0^{\pi/2} - \frac{2}{\pi n} \int_0^{\pi/2} \cos 2nx \, dx$$

$$= \frac{4}{\pi}\left[\frac{\pi}{8n} \cos \pi n + \frac{\pi}{8n} \right] - \frac{1}{\pi n^2} [\sin 2nx]_0^{\pi/2}$$

$$= \frac{1}{2n} (\cos \pi n + 1)$$

$$= \frac{1}{2n} [(-1)^n + 1] \qquad \text{for } n = 1, 2, 3, \ldots .$$

Hence,

$$f(x) = \frac{\sin 4x}{2} + \frac{\sin 8x}{4} + \frac{\sin 12x}{6} + \frac{\sin 16x}{8} + \cdots .$$

EXERCISES

1. Find the Fourier cosine series for the function in Example 2.
2. Find the Fourier series expansion for the following function:

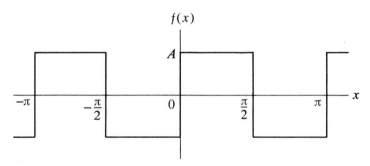

DRAWING 4

In Exercises 3 through 6, find the Fourier series expansion for $f(x)$.

3. $f(x) = 1$ for $0 < x < 1$,
      $= -1$ for $1 < x < 2$.
4. $f(x) = x$ for $0 < x < 1$,
      $= 0$ for $1 < x < 2$.
5. $f(x) = x - x^2$ for $-1 < x < 1$.
6. $f(x) = x^3$ for $0 < x < 2\pi$.

7. Show that if a is not an integer, then

$$\sin ax = \frac{2 \sin a\pi}{\pi} \left[\frac{\sin x}{(1^2 - a^2)} - \frac{2 \sin 2x}{(2^2 - a^2)} + \frac{3 \sin 3x}{(3^2 - a^2)} - \cdots \right].$$

8. Given $f(x) = kx + 1$:
   (a) Find the Fourier series expansion for $-\pi < x < \pi$;
   (b) Find the Fourier series expansion for $0 < x < 2\pi$;
   (c) Find the Fourier cosine series expansion for $0 < x < \pi$;
   (d) Find the Fourier sine series expansion for $0 < x < \pi$.

7. HARMONIC ANALYSIS

We have examined the problem of expressing a periodic function $f(x)$ as an infinite Fourier series. If $f(x)$ is given by a table for equidistant values of x, or if the integrals involved in the expressions for the Fourier coefficients cannot be integrated, then $f(x)$ may be approximated by a trigonometric series of the form

$$T(x) = a_0 + a_1 \cos x + a_2 \cos 2x + \cdots + a_n \cos nx$$
$$+ b_1 \sin x + b_2 \sin 2x + \cdots + b_n \sin nx. \qquad \textbf{7.17}$$

The problem of determining the a_i's and b_i's is called *harmonic analysis.*

Let $f(x)$ have a period of 2π (from $-\pi$ to π). In some cases, a transformation of variable may be necessary to adjust for this period. Consider the interval from $-\pi$ to π divided into $2k$ equidistant subintervals.† We shall designate the points of division by x_j where

$$x_j = \frac{j\pi}{k}.$$

By the method of least squares, we desire to determine the a_i's and b_i's necessary to minimize the expression

$$\sum_{j=-k}^{k-1} \left[f(x_j) - \sum_{i=0}^{n} (a_i \cos ix_j + b_i \sin ix_j) \right]^2. \qquad \textbf{7.18}$$

Differentiating partially with respect to the a_i's and b_i's of (7.18), we obtain the set of $2n + 1$ normal equations:

$$\sum_{i=0}^{n} \left[a_i \sum_{j=-k}^{k-1} \cos ix_j \cos rx_j + b_i \sum_{j=-k}^{k-1} \sin ix_j \cos rx_j \right] = \sum_{j=-k}^{k-1} f(x_j) \cos rx_j \qquad \textbf{7.19}$$

and

$$\sum_{i=0}^{n} \left[a_i \sum_{j=-k}^{k-1} \cos ix_j \sin rx_j + b_i \sum_{j=-k}^{k-1} \sin ix_j \sin rx_j \right] = \sum_{j=-k}^{k-1} f(x_j) \sin rx_j \qquad \textbf{7.20}$$

for $r = 0, 1, 2, \ldots, n$.

† It is understood that $k > n$. If $k = n$, it can be shown that b_n should be excluded from the expression for $T(x)$.

The following trigonometric identities are valid for integral values of i and r not less than zero and not greater than k:

$$\sum_{j=-k}^{k-1} \sin ix_j \cos rx_j = 0; \tag{7.21}$$

$$\sum_{j=-k}^{k-1} \cos ix_j \cos rx_j = \begin{cases} 0 & \text{if } i \neq r, \\ k & \text{if } i = r \neq 0, k, \\ 2k & \text{if } i = r = 0, k; \end{cases} \tag{7.22}$$

$$\sum_{j=-k}^{k-1} \sin ix_j \sin rx_j = \begin{cases} 0 & \text{if } i \neq r, \\ k & \text{if } i = r \neq 0, k, \\ 0 & \text{if } i = r = 0, k. \end{cases} \tag{7.23}$$

Making use of equations (7.21), (7.22), and (7.23), we may reduce the normal equations expressed by (7.19) and (7.20) such that the following relationships for the Fourier coefficients are obtained:

$$a_0 = \frac{1}{2k} \sum_{j=-k}^{k-1} f(x_j); \tag{7.24}$$

$$a_i = \frac{1}{k} \sum_{j=-k}^{k-1} f(x_j) \cos ix_j \qquad \text{for } 0 < i < k; \tag{7.25}$$

$$b_i = \frac{1}{k} \sum_{j=-k}^{k-1} f(x_j) \sin ix_j \qquad \text{for } 0 < i < k. \tag{7.26}$$

Note that if $i = k$, equation (7.25) becomes

$$a_k = \frac{1}{2k} \sum_{j=-k}^{k-1} f(x_j) \cos kx_j \tag{7.27}$$

as a result of (7.22).

When the number of equidistant values of x_j are either 12 or 24, that is, when k equals 6 or 12, respectively, effective grouping of terms may be utilized to reduce the computation. In addition, such choices involve simple evaluations of the sine and cosine functions. Elaborate schemes for the harmonic analysis of the twelve ordinate and twenty-four ordinate cases are available in numerous texts and journals. We shall not concern ourselves with such devices in our introductory study.

The question of whether or not one should employ the method of harmonic analysis to a set of empirical data can be partially answered by means of a graph of the data. If the graph shows a periodic tendency, a harmonic analysis should be considered. Additional information such as that which one obtains from a difference table, a logarithmic plot, or a semilogarithmic plot should be utilized in arriving at the final decision concerning the interpolation method to be employed.

EXAMPLE. Find an empirical periodic function which fits the following data:

$x°$	-180	-150	-120	-90	-60	-30	0	30	60	90	120	150
y	8	15	20	20	24	16	9	4	0	-6	-10	-3

Solution: Since the function is periodic, we assume $y = 8$ at $x = 180°$, and $k = 6$. Our trigonometric approximation function is of the form

$$T(x) = a_0 + a_1 \cos x + a_2 \cos 2x + \cdots + a_6 \cos 6x$$
$$+ b_1 \sin x + b_2 \sin 2x + \cdots + b_5 \sin 5x.$$

Tables A, B, C, and D are constructed.

TABLE A

$x°$	$\cos x$	$\cos 2x$	$\cos 3x$	$\cos 4x$	$\cos 5x$	$\cos 6x$
-180	-1.000000	1.0	-1	1.0	-1.000000	1
-150	-0.866025	0.5	0	-0.5	0.866025	-1
-120	-0.500000	-0.5	1	-0.5	-0.500000	1
-90	0.000000	-1.0	0	1.0	0.000000	-1
-60	0.500000	-0.5	-1	-0.5	0.500000	1
-30	0.866025	0.5	0	-0.5	-0.866025	-1
0	1.000000	1.0	1	1.0	1.000000	1
30	0.866025	0.5	0	-0.5	-0.866025	-1
60	0.500000	-0.5	-1	-0.5	0.500000	1
90	0.000000	-1.0	0	1.0	0.000000	-1
120	-0.500000	-0.5	1	-0.5	-0.500000	1
150	-0.866025	0.5	0	-0.5	0.866025	-1

TABLE B

$x°$	y	$\sin x$	$\sin 2x$	$\sin 3x$	$\sin 4x$	$\sin 5x$
-180	8	0.000000	0.000000	0	0.000000	0.000000
-150	15	-0.500000	0.866025	-1	0.866025	-0.500000
-120	20	-0.866025	0.866025	0	-0.866025	0.866025
-90	20	-1.000000	0.000000	1	0.000000	-1.000000
-60	24	-0.866025	-0.866025	0	0.866025	0.866025
-30	16	-0.500000	-0.866025	-1	-0.866025	-0.500000
0	9	0.000000	0.000000	0	0.000000	0.000000
30	4	0.500000	0.866025	1	0.866025	0.500000
60	0	0.866025	0.866025	0	-0.866025	-0.866025
90	-6	1.000000	0.000000	-1	0.000000	1.000000
120	-10	0.866025	-0.866025	0	0.866025	-0.866025
150	-3	0.500000	-0.866025	1	-0.866025	0.500000

TABLE C

$x°$	$y \cos x$	$y \cos 2x$	$y \cos 3x$	$y \cos 4x$	$y \cos 5x$	$y \cos 6x$
−180	−8.000000	8.0	−8	8.0	−8.000000	8
−150	−12.990375	7.5	0	−7.5	12.990375	−15
−120	−10.000000	−10.0	20	−10.0	−10.000000	20
−90	0.000000	−20.0	0	20.0	0.000000	−20
−60	12.000000	−12.0	−24	−12.0	12.000000	24
−30	13.856400	8.0	0	−8.0	−13.856400	−16
0	9.000000	9.0	9	9.0	9.000000	9
30	3.464100	2.0	0	−2.0	−3.464100	−4
60	0.000000	0.0	0	0.0	0.000000	0
90	0.000000	6.0	0	−6.0	0.000000	6
120	5.000000	5.0	−10	5.0	5.000000	−10
150	2.598075	−1.5	0	1.5	−2.598075	3

TABLE D

$x°$	$y \sin x$	$y \sin 2x$	$y \sin 3x$	$y \sin 4x$	$y \sin 5x$
−180	0.000000	0.000000	0	0.000000	0.000000
−150	−7.500000	12.990375	−15	12.990375	−7.500000
−120	−17.320500	17.320500	0	−17.320500	17.320500
−90	−20.000000	0.000000	20	0.000000	−20.000000
−60	−20.784600	−20.784600	0	20.784600	20.784600
−30	−8.000000	−13.856400	−16	−13.856400	−8.000000
0	0.000000	0.000000	0	0.000000	0.000000
30	2.000000	3.464100	4	3.464100	2.000000
60	0.000000	0.000000	0	0.000000	0.000000
90	−6.000000	0.000000	6	0.000000	−6.000000
120	−8.660250	8.660250	0	−8.660250	8.660250
150	−1.500000	2.598075	−3	2.598075	−1.500000

Now,

$$a_0 = \tfrac{1}{12} \sum y = 8.083333,$$
$$a_1 = \tfrac{1}{6} \sum y \cos x = 2.488033,$$
$$a_2 = \tfrac{1}{6} \sum y \cos 2x = 0.333333,$$
$$a_3 = \tfrac{1}{6} \sum y \cos 3x = -2.166667,$$
$$a_4 = \tfrac{1}{6} \sum y \cos 4x = -0.333333,$$
$$a_5 = \tfrac{1}{6} \sum y \cos 5x = 0.178633,$$
$$a_6 = \tfrac{1}{12} \sum y \cos 6x = 0.416667,$$

and

$$b_1 = \tfrac{1}{6} \sum y \sin x \; = -14.627558,$$
$$b_2 = \tfrac{1}{6} \sum y \sin 2x = 1.732050,$$
$$b_3 = \tfrac{1}{6} \sum y \sin 3x = -0.666667,$$
$$b_4 = \tfrac{1}{6} \sum y \sin 4x = 0.000000,$$
$$b_5 = \tfrac{1}{6} \sum y \sin 5x = 0.960892.$$

Hence,

$$T(x) = 8.083333 + 2.488033 \cos x + 0.333333 \cos 2x$$
$$- 2.166667 \cos 3x - 0.333333 \cos 4x + 0.178633 \cos 5x$$
$$+ 0.416667 \cos 6x - 14.627558 \sin x + 1.732050 \sin 2x$$
$$- 0.666667 \sin 3x + 0.960892 \sin 5x.$$

Table E indicates how accurately $T(x)$ approximates y.

TABLE E

$x°$	y	$T(x)$
-180	8	8.000001
-150	15	14.999999
-120	20	19.999986
-90	20	19.999999
-60	24	23.999989
-30	16	15.999999
0	9	8.999999
30	4	3.999996
60	0	0.000011
90	-6	-5.999999
120	-10	-9.999986
150	-3	-2.999998

EXERCISES

In the following exercises, determine by means of a harmonic analysis a periodic function which approximates the given data:

1.

$x°$	-180	-150	-120	-90	-60	-30	0	30	60	90	120	150
y	0	1	3	5	4	4	4	4	3	2	2	1

2.

$x°$	0	30	60	90	120	150	180
y	0	1	2	4	4	1	0

Consider y as an even function of x.

3.

x	0	1	2	3	4	5	6
y	10	18	36	17	-5	-14	10

Use a transformation of variables.

8

Numerical Solutions of Ordinary Differential Equations

I. INTRODUCTION

Physical problems involving instantaneous rates of change may be described mathematically by equations involving variables and their derivatives. Such expressions are called *differential equations*.

Several known exact methods of solution exist for the most elementary classes of ordinary differential equations. An *ordinary differential equation* is an equation involving one independent variable x and derivatives of the dependent variable y; that is, an ordinary differential equation is of the form

$$f(x, y, y', \ldots, y^{(n)}) = 0, \qquad \textbf{8.1}$$

where $y^{(n)}$ denotes the nth-order derivative of y with respect to x. The differential equation of (8.1) is called an *nth-order differential equation*. Recall that a *general implicit solution* of an nth-order differential equation is of the form

$$g(x, y, c_1, c_2, \ldots, c_n) = 0, \qquad \textbf{8.2}$$

where $c_1, c_2, \ldots, c_n$ represent n arbitrary constants. If n independent *initial conditions* are imposed upon (8.1), a *particular implicit solution* is of the form

$$h(x, y) = 0. \qquad \textbf{8.3}$$

However, exact methods of solution do not exist for the vast majority of the classes of ordinary differential equations. Therefore, it is necessary to devise numerical procedures for the solution of such equations. In this chapter, we shall discuss and illustrate some of the fundamental numerical methods for the solution of ordinary differential equations with initial conditions (sometimes called *boundary conditions*). We shall be primarily concerned with first-order differential equations.

A numerical solution to an ordinary differential equation (8.1) with initial conditions is a set of numerical values,

$$\{(x, y) \,|\, f(x, y, y', \ldots, y^{(n)}) = 0\},$$

over some domain of the independent variable. Numerical methods for the solution of ordinary differential equations essentially involve step-by-step calculations. A succession of points on a particular integral curve (initial boundary problem) are approximated, usually involving a considerable amount of computation. The use of some form of a digital computer will, generally, save considerable labor and time. The availability of a computer eases the computational burden placed upon the person faced with the problem of obtaining a numerical solution, thereby allowing that person to concern himself with the relative merits of the methods available. Certain numerical methods are more applicable to computers than others.

2. THE GRAPHICAL METHOD

Consider the problem of finding an approximation to the particular solution at $x = x_1$ of the first-order differential equation

$$y' = f(x, y) \qquad\qquad 8.4$$

satisfying the point (x_0, y_0). Assuming that $f(x, y)$ is a single-valued continuous function in some region of the xy-plane, then, for each point (x, y) in the region,

$$f(x, y) = c \qquad\qquad 8.5$$

where c is some constant. The set of curves represented by (8.5) for different choices of c are called *isoclines*. At each point on a particular curve, we may associate geometrically a short line segment with slope c. These short line segments will be parallel and represent tangents to the family of general solutions of (8.4). If a sufficient number of isoclines are constructed, along with their associated line elements at reasonable intervals, the general solution functions to (8.4) may be approximated graphically by a set of curves. Each curve may be obtained by choosing a line segment on an isocline and following that line segment to a line segment of a neighboring isocline, and continuing in this manner. Each curve will cross many isoclines in the region of the xy-plane under examination. Each curve represents a member of the general solution set for (8.4) and is called an *integral curve*. The construction of an integral curve by drawing its tangents at a set of points in some region of the xy-plane is analogous to the process of integration of the differential equation.

The integral curve passing through the point (x_0, y_0) is the particular solution curve desired. The line $x = x_1$ intersects this integral curve at approximately $y = y_1$, the desired particular numerical solution. Indeed, if we only wish to determine a particular numerical solution, a complete set of isoclines and their associated line elements are unnecessary. The intersection of a short line segment drawn at (x_0, y_0) with slope $f(x_0, y_0)$ and the line $x = x_1$ will determine an approximation to y_1. The method of the next section is geometrically described by this approach.

In principle, the graphical method is extremely simple. However, the accuracy of the method depends upon the amount of detail used in graphing. In addition, it should be noted that another disadvantage of the graphical method lies in the fact that the isoclines may be very difficult to construct.

EXAMPLE 1.   Find the set of integral curves which are solutions to the first-order differential equation

$$y' = - \frac{x}{y}.$$

Solution: Now, according to (8.5), the isoclines for the differential equation $y' = - \dfrac{x}{y}$ are given by $- \dfrac{x}{y} = c$; that is, the isoclines are represented by a family of lines $y = - \dfrac{1}{c} x$. Each line passes through the origin and has slope equal to

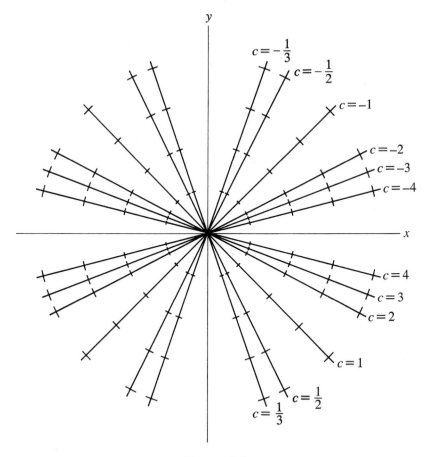

FIGURE 8.1

$-\dfrac{1}{c}$. On each line $y = -\dfrac{1}{c}x$, we associate at a number of points a set of short parallel line segments with slope c. The set of integral curves representing the general solution of the given differential equation consists of the set of concentric circles with center at the origin. That is, the general solution to the differential equation $y' = -\dfrac{x}{y}$ is $x^2 + y^2 = k$, where k is some arbitrary constant.

EXAMPLE 2.   Find a numerical approximation to the particular solution at $x = 3.2$ of the first-order differential equation in Example 1 satisfying the point $(3, 4)$.

   Solution: At $(3, 4)$, the particular integral curve desired has slope equal to $-\frac{3}{4}$ and is perpendicular to the isocline $y = \frac{4}{3}x$. The equation of the tangent line to the integral curve at $(3, 4)$ is $y - 4 = -\frac{3}{4}(x - 3)$; that is, $3x + 4y - 25 = 0$. This tangent line and the line $x = 3.2$ intersect at the point $P(3.2, 3.85)$. Hence, $y = 3.85$ is a numerical approximation to the particular solution at $x = 3.2$. Note that the exact solution at $x = 3.2$ is given by $\sqrt{25 - (3.2)^2} = 3.84$, correct to the nearest hundredth of a unit.

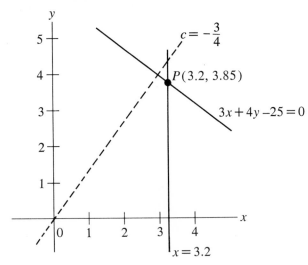

FIGURE 8.2

EXERCISES

In Exercises 1 through 8, sketch a set of isoclines for $c = 0$, $\pm\frac{1}{4}$, $\pm\frac{1}{3}$, $\pm\frac{1}{2}$, ± 1, ± 2, ± 3, ± 4 for the given differential equation. Associate the appropriate short parallel line segments with each isocline at reasonable intervals. Indicate the general solution set by several representative integral curves.

1. $y' = \dfrac{y}{x}$.   **2.** $y' = -\dfrac{x}{4y}$.   **3.** $y' = x - y$.   **4.** $y' = 2 - y$.

5. $y' = 2x.$ **6.** $y' = x^2 - y^2.$

7. $y' = x + y^2.$ **8.** $y' = \dfrac{x + y}{x - y}.$

In Exercises 9 through 12, find a numerical approximation to the particular solution at $x = 1.5$ of the differential equation in the stated exercise with initial condition $y = 1$ when $x = 2$.

9. Exercise 2.   **10.** Exercise 3.

11. Exercise 4.   **12.** Exercise 5.

3. EULER'S METHOD

One of the simplest numerical procedures for obtaining particular solutions of the first-order differential equation $y' = f(x, y)$ in a relatively small region of the xy-plane about a given point (x_0, y_0) is attributed to Euler. The graphical method which was studied in Section 8.2 for solving a first-order differential equation is the geometrical equivalent of Euler's method.

Euler's method involves a linear extrapolation along the tangent line to an integral curve passing through (x_0, y_0). The first step of this method is to determine an increment Δy of the dependent variable for some arbitrary increment Δx of the independent variable from the given point (x_0, y_0). Since

$$\frac{\Delta y}{\Delta x} \approx f(x, y), \qquad\qquad \textbf{8.6}$$

$$\Delta y \approx f(x, y) \, \Delta x. \qquad\qquad \textbf{8.7}$$

Then

$$y_1 = y_0 + \Delta y_0 \approx y_0 + f(x_0, y_0) \, \Delta x_0, \qquad\qquad \textbf{8.8}$$

where (x_1, y_1) represents the coordinates of a second point on the integral curve $y' = f(x, y)$ passing through (x_0, y_0) such that $x_1 = x_0 + \Delta x_0$. A repetition of the process yields an approximation to a third point (x_2, y_2) on the integral curve, where $x_2 = x_1 + \Delta x_1$ and

$$y_2 = y_1 + \Delta y_1 \approx y_1 + f(x_1, y_1) \, \Delta x_1.$$

Note that the y_1 used here is equal to the approximation obtained in (8.8) since we cannot obtain the exact value of y_1. In general, an *approximation* to the coordinates of an $(n + 1)$th point on the integral curve is obtained by using the recursion formulas

$$x_n = x_{n-1} + \Delta x_{n-1}, \qquad\qquad \textbf{8.9}$$

$$y_n = y_{n-1} + \Delta y_{n-1} \approx y_{n-1} + f(x_{n-1}, y_{n-1}) \, \Delta x_{n-1}, \qquad\qquad \textbf{8.10}$$

and is called *Euler's method*. In calculating a set of approximations to the points on a particular integral curve, Δx_i is usually chosen as some convenient constant for all values of i. Hereafter, we shall omit the subscripts for Δx_i in such instances.

Furthermore, we shall write

$$y_n = y_{n-1} + f(x_{n-1}, y_{n-1}) \Delta x \qquad \textbf{8.11}$$

when using Euler's method, noting that y_n is an approximation. In discussing other numerical procedures, it will often be convenient to use the equal sign for an approximation. The context of the discussion will usually denote when an approximation is implied.

EXAMPLE 1.   Approximate the particular solutions over the interval $0 \le x \le 1$ of the differential equation $y' = y - x$ through (0, 2). Let $\Delta x = 0.1$.

Solution: Now, $f(x, y) = y - x$. Then, using formula (8.11) with $(x_0, y_0) = $ (0, 2) and $\Delta x = 0.1$,

$$x_1 = 0.1, \quad y_1 = 2 + (2 - 0)(0.1) = 2.2,$$
$$x_2 = 0.2, \quad y_2 = 2.2 + (2.2 - 0.1)(0.1) = 2.41,$$
$$x_3 = 0.3, \quad y_3 = 2.41 + (2.41 - 0.2)(0.1) = 2.631,$$
$$x_4 = 0.4, \quad y_4 = 2.631 + (2.631 - 0.3)(0.1) = 2.864,$$
$$x_5 = 0.5, \quad y_5 = 2.864 + (2.864 - 0.4)(0.1) = 3.110,$$
$$x_6 = 0.6, \quad y_6 = 3.110 + (3.110 - 0.5)(0.1) = 3.371,$$
$$x_7 = 0.7, \quad y_7 = 3.371 + (3.371 - 0.6)(0.1) = 3.648,$$
$$x_8 = 0.8, \quad y_8 = 3.648 + (3.648 - 0.7)(0.1) = 3.943,$$
$$x_9 = 0.9, \quad y_9 = 3.943 + (3.943 - 0.8)(0.1) = 4.257,$$
$$x_{10} = 1.0, \quad y_{10} = 4.257 + (4.257 - 0.9)(0.1) = 4.593.$$

The exact solution to the given first-order differential equation with its initial condition is $y = e^x + x + 1$. Table A represents a comparison between the set of exact points on the domain $0 \le x \le 1$ at 0.1 intervals and the set of approximations obtained using Euler's method. Values used are correct to the nearest thousandth of a unit.

TABLE A

x	0	0.1	0.2	0.3	0.4	0.5	0.6	0.7	0.8	0.9	1.0
y (approx.)	2.000	2.200	2.410	2.631	2.864	3.110	3.371	3.648	3.943	4.257	4.593
y (exact)	2.000	2.205	2.421	2.650	2.892	3.149	3.422	3.714	4.026	4.360	4.718

Notice that the approximations at the end of the domain are rather poor. This is a typical occurrence; Euler's method is useful and accurate over a relatively small domain and with relatively small increments of the independent variable. In general, the accuracy obtained by Euler's method may be increased somewhat if smaller increments of the independent variable are chosen over the domain of integration.

In order to illustrate geometrically the increase in accuracy usually obtained by choosing smaller increments of the independent variable, consider the integral curve $y' = f(x, y)$ satisfying the point $P(x_0, y_0)$ in Figure 8.3. Assume that the value of the curvature of the integral curve remains fixed with regard to sign in the interval $x_0 \leq x \leq x_0 + h$.

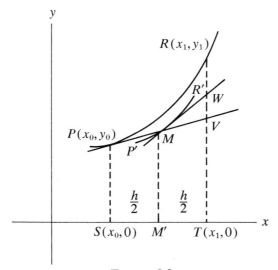

FIGURE 8.3

Let $R(x_1, y_1)$ be the point on the curve associated with $x_1 = x_0 + h$. Then y_1 is represented geometrically by the length of the line segment RT. Using Euler's method with $\Delta x = h$, an approximation to y_1 is represented by the length of the line segment VT; that is, the ordinate value when $x = x_0 + h$ of the tangent line at P to the integral curve PR. A better approximation to y_1 may be obtained by the following procedure. Let the interval from x_0 to x_1 be divided into two subintervals each of length $\dfrac{h}{2}$. Use Euler's method to obtain an approximation to y when $x = x_0 + \Delta x$, where $\Delta x = \dfrac{h}{2}$. This approximation, represented by MM', is equal to the ordinate value when $x = x_0 + \dfrac{h}{2}$ of the tangent line at P to the integral curve PR. The point M lies on an integral curve $P'R'$. Use Euler's method again to obtain an approximation to y when $x = x_1 = \left(x_0 + \dfrac{h}{2}\right) + \dfrac{h}{2}$ on the integral curve $P'R'$. This approximation, represented by WT, is equal to the ordinate value when $x = x_1$ of the tangent line at M to the integral curve $P'R'$. It is evident from the geometric description that WT is a better approximation to RT than is VT. Careful note should be made that under Euler's method the function is approximated by a linear function in each interval Δx. The degree of accuracy desired and the amount of labor and time involved are factors which influence the choice of a Δx.

EXAMPLE 2.   Approximate the particular solution at $x = 0.4$ of the differential equation $y' = 2x - y + 2$ through $(0, 1)$ using **(a)** $\Delta x = 0.2$; **(b)** $\Delta x = 0.1$. Compare the results of **(a)** and **(b)** with the exact particular solution.

Solution: Now, $f(x, y) = 2x - y + 2$ with $(x_0, y_0) = (0, 1)$.
(a) Using $\Delta x = 0.2$,

$$x_1 = 0.2, \; y_1 = 1 + [2(0) - (1) + 2](0.2) = 1.2,$$
$$x_2 = 0.4, \; y_2 = 1.2 + [2(0.2) - (1.2) + 2](0.2) = 1.44.$$

(b) Using $\Delta x = 0.1$,

$$x_1 = 0.1, \; y_1 = 1 + [2(0) - (1) + 2](0.1) = 1.1,$$
$$x_2 = 0.2, \; y_2 = 1.1 + [2(0.1) - (1.1) + 2](0.1) = 1.21,$$
$$x_3 = 0.3, \; y_3 = 1.21 + [2(0.2) - (1.21) + 2](0.1) = 1.329,$$
$$x_4 = 0.4, \; y_4 = 1.329 + [2(0.3) - (1.329) + 2](0.1) = 1.4561.$$

Therefore, by Euler's method using $\Delta x = 0.1$, an approximation to y when $x = 0.4$ is 1.4561.

It can be shown that the exact solution of the given differential equation is $y = 2x + e^{-x}$. Hence, when $x = 0.4$, $y = 1.4703$, correct to the nearest ten-thousandth of a unit. The numerical solution of **(b)** is a better approximation than the numerical solution of **(a)**.

The step-by-step integration scheme outlined in Euler's method may be applied to higher-order differential equations. For example, in the case of a second-order differential equation

$$y'' = f(x, y, y') \tag{8.12}$$

with initial conditions $y' = y_0'$ and $y = y_0$ when $x = x_0$, the equation may be considered equivalent to the system of two simultaneous differential equations

$$\begin{cases} y' = z, \\ z' = f(x, y, z), \end{cases} \tag{8.13}$$

satisfying $(x, y, z) = (x_0, y_0, y_0')$. A particular solution to the system of (8.13) when $x = x_1$ consists of a pair of values z_1 (or y_1') and y_1 which satisfy the equations simultaneously. An approximation to the particular solutions z_1 and y_1 may be obtained simultaneously by employing Euler's method with increment Δx, where $\Delta x = x_1 - x_0$. Successive particular solutions z_2 and y_2 may be approximated simultaneously by using the preceding approximations z_1 (or y_1') and y_1 and Euler's method again.

EXAMPLE 3.   Use Euler's method to approximate the particular solution at $x = 0.1$ of the differential equation $y'' = 4y - 2xy'$ if $y' = 0.5$ and $y = 0.2$ when $x = 0$. Use $\Delta x = 0.05$ and consider the approximation to the nearest thousandth of a unit.

Solution: The second-order differential equation $y'' = 4y - 2xy'$ is equivalent to the system of two simultaneous differential equations

$$\begin{cases} y' = z, \\ z' = 4y - 2xz, \end{cases}$$

where $(x_0, y_0, z_0) = (0, 0.2, 0.5)$. Now, using Euler's method,

$$\Delta y = z \, \Delta x, \qquad\qquad\qquad \Delta z = (4y - 2xz) \, \Delta x,$$

$$\begin{aligned} y_1 &= y_0 + \Delta y_0 \\ &= y_0 + z_0 \, \Delta x_0 \\ &= 0.2 + (0.5)(0.05) \\ &= 0.225, \end{aligned} \qquad\qquad \begin{aligned} z_1 &= z_0 + \Delta z_0 \\ &= z_0 + (4y_0 - 2x_0 z_0) \, \Delta x_0 \\ &= 0.5 + [4(0.2) - 2(0)(0.5)](0.05) \\ &= 0.54, \end{aligned}$$

and $(x_1, y_1, z_1) = (0.05, 0.225, 0.54)$. Using Euler's method again,

$$\begin{aligned} y_2 &= y_1 + \Delta y_1 \\ &= y_1 + z_1 \, \Delta x_1 \\ &= 0.225 + 0.54(0.05) \\ &= 0.252. \end{aligned}$$

Hence, by Euler's method, $y = 0.252$ when $x = 0.1$.

EXAMPLE 4.   Use Euler's method to approximate a set of particular solutions of the system of simultaneous differential equations

$$\begin{cases} y' = x + z^2, \\ z' = y - x, \end{cases}$$

over the interval $0 \le x \le 1.5$ given that $(x_0, y_0, z_0) = (0, 0, 1)$. Use $\Delta x = 0.5$.

Solution: Let $f(x, y, z) = x + z^2$ and $g(x, y, z) = y - x$. Then, using Euler's method, $\Delta y = f(x, y, z) \, \Delta x$ and $\Delta z = g(x, y, z) \, \Delta x$. Hence,

$$\begin{aligned} y_1 &= y_0 + \Delta y_0 \\ &= y_0 + f(x_0, y_0, z_0) \, \Delta x_0 \\ &= 0 + (1)(0.5) \\ &= 0.5, \end{aligned} \qquad\qquad \begin{aligned} z_1 &= z_0 + \Delta z_0 \\ &= z_0 + g(x_0, y_0, z_0) \, \Delta x_0 \\ &= 1 + (0)(0.5) \\ &= 1, \end{aligned}$$

and $(x_1, y_1, z_1) = (0.5, 0.5, 1)$. Repeating the process,

$$\begin{aligned} y_2 &= y_1 + \Delta y_1 \\ &= y_1 + f(x_1, y_1, z_1) \, \Delta x_1 \\ &= 0.5 + (0.5 + 1^2)(0.5) \\ &= 1.25, \end{aligned} \qquad\qquad \begin{aligned} z_2 &= z_1 + \Delta z_1 \\ &= z_1 + g(x_1, y_1, z_1) \, \Delta x_1 \\ &= 1 + (0.5 - 0.5)(0.5) \\ &= 1, \end{aligned}$$

and $(x_2, y_2, z_2) = (1, 1.25, 1)$. Repeating the process again,

$$y_3 = y_2 + \Delta y_2 \qquad\qquad\qquad z_3 = z_2 + \Delta z_2$$
$$= y_2 + f(x_2, y_2, z_2)\,\Delta x_2 \qquad = z_2 + g(x_2, y_2, z_2)\,\Delta x_2$$
$$= 1.25 + (1 + 1^2)(0.5) \qquad\quad = 1 + (1.25 - 1)(0.5)$$
$$= 2.25, \qquad\qquad\qquad\quad = 1.125,$$

and $(x_3, y_3, z_3) = (1.5, 2.25, 1.125)$. Table B contains a summary of the particular solutions of the given system of simultaneous differential equations.

TABLE B

x	0	0.5	1	1.5
y	0	0.5	1.25	2.25
z	1	1	1	1.125

4. THE MODIFIED EULER METHOD

The inherent error of Euler's method when applied to the solution of a differential equation with initial conditions whose integral curve has a constant positive or negative curvature was discussed in the preceding section. Euler's method may be modified to obtain somewhat better results.

The first step of the modified Euler method in determining the particular solution y_1 to equation (8.4) with its initial condition is the same as in Euler's method; that is,

$$y_{11} = y_0 + \Delta y_0 = y_0 + f(x_0, y_0)\,\Delta x, \qquad \textbf{8.14}$$

where the second subscript indicates that this is a first approximation to y_1. Next, y_{11} is used to obtain an approximation to $f(x, y)$ at the end of the interval, which becomes $f(x_1, y_{11})$. A second approximation to y_1, denoted by y_{12}, is obtained by using the average of the derivatives at the beginning and at the end of the interval as a measure of the derivative throughout the interval; that is,

$$y_{12} = y_0 + \frac{f(x_0, y_0) + f(x_1, y_{11})}{2}\,\Delta x. \qquad \textbf{8.15}$$

The improved value y_{12} is now used to determine a second approximation to $f(x, y)$ at the end of the interval. The process of averaging the derivatives at both ends of the interval is continued in order to obtain improved approximations to y_1 until two successive approximations agree to the desired degree of accuracy. In general, the nth approximation to y_1 is given by the recursion formula

$$y_{1n} = y_0 + \frac{f(x_0, y_0) + f(x_1, y_{1n-1})}{2}\,\Delta x \qquad \textbf{8.16}$$

and is known as the *modified Euler method*.

EXAMPLE. Use the modified Euler method to approximate the particular solution at $x = 0.4$ of the differential equation $y' = 2x - y + 2$ through $(0, 1)$. Consider the approximation to the nearest thousandth of a unit.

Solution: Now, $f(x, y) = 2x - y + 2$ with $(x_0, y_0) = (0, 1)$. Then

$$f(x_0, y_0) = 1 \quad \text{and} \quad \Delta x = 0.4.$$

Hence, using (8.14),

$$y_{11} = 1 + (1)(0.4) = 1.4,$$

$$f(x_1, y_{11}) = 2(0.4) - 1.4 + 2 = 1.4.$$

Using (8.15),

$$y_{12} = 1 + \frac{1 + 1.4}{2}(0.4) = 1.48,$$

$$f(x_1, y_{12}) = 2(0.4) - 1.48 + 2 = 1.32.$$

Using (8.16) for $n = 3$, 4, and 5,

$$y_{13} = 1 + \frac{1 + 1.32}{2}(0.4) = 1.464,$$

$$f(x_1, y_{13}) = 2(0.4) - 1.464 + 2 = 1.336,$$

$$y_{14} = 1 + \frac{1 + 1.336}{2}(0.4) = 1.467,$$

$$f(x_1, y_{14}) = 2(0.4) - 1.467 + 2 = 1.333,$$

$$y_{15} = 1 + \frac{1 + 1.333}{2}(0.4) = 1.467.$$

Since y_{14} and y_{15} agree to the nearest thousandth of a unit, the process is terminated and 1.467 is accepted as a numerical approximation to y when $x = 0.4$. Note that 1.467 is a better approximation to the exact solution than that obtained by Euler's method with $\Delta x = 0.1$. (See Example 2 of Section 8.3.)

EXERCISES

In Exercises 1 through 6, use Euler's method to find numerical approximations to the particular solutions of the differential equation with the stated initial conditions. If possible, compare the approximations with the exact results to the nearest thousandth of a unit.

1. At $x = 1.3$ for $y' = \dfrac{y + 1}{x}$ through $(1, 0)$.

2. At $x = 0.5$ for $y' = x + y$ through $(0, 0)$.

3. At $x = 1$ for $y' = \dfrac{1}{1 + x^2}$ through $(0, 1)$.

4. At $x = 0.1$ for $y' = y + e^{2x}$ through $(0, 2)$.

5. Over the interval $0 \leq x \leq 0.4$ for $y' = x + y^2$ through $(0, 1)$. Use $\Delta x = 0.1$.

6. Over the interval $0 \leq x \leq 0.5$ for $(1 + x)y' = 3y$ through $(0, 1)$. Use $\Delta x = 0.1$.

7. Use Euler's method to find a numerical approximation to the particular solution at $x = 1.5$ of the second-order differential equation $y'' = x + yy'$ if $y' = 0$ and $y = 1$ when $x = 0$. Use $\Delta x = 0.5$.

8. Use Euler's method to approximate a set of particular solutions of the system of simultaneous differential equations

$$\begin{cases} y' = z - x, \\ z' = x + y, \end{cases}$$

over the interval $0 \leq x \leq 1$ given that $(x_0, y_0, z_0) = (0, 1, 2)$. Use $\Delta x = 0.5$.

In Exercises 9 through 12, use the modified Euler method and do the indicated exercises of this section. Consider the approximations to the nearest thousandth of a unit.

9. Exercise 2.   10. Exercise 3.

11. Exercise 4.   12. Exercise 6.

5. SOLUTION BY SERIES

An important class of numerical methods for the solution of differential equations involves the use of power series. In particular, the Taylor series expansion of a function is the basis for many numerical methods of solution.

Consider again the problem of obtaining a particular solution of the differential equation of (8.4). Assume that $f(x, y)$ is a single-valued function possessing derivatives of higher-order in some region of the xy-plane about the point (x_0, y_0); that is, assume the general solution of (8.4) has a Taylor series expansion about the point (x_0, y_0). Then, the general solution is of the form

$$y = y_0 + (x - x_0)f(x_0, y_0) + \frac{(x - x_0)^2 f'(x_0, y_0)}{2!} + \cdots$$

$$+ \frac{(x - x_0)^n f^{(n-1)}(x_0, y_0)}{n!} + \cdots . \qquad \textbf{8.17}$$

Letting $x = x_1$; that is, $x = x_0 + \Delta x$, equation (8.17) becomes

$$y_1 = y_0 + (\Delta x)f(x_0, y_0) + \frac{(\Delta x)^2 f'(x_0, y_0)}{2!} + \cdots + \frac{(\Delta x)^n f^{(n-1)}(x_0, y_0)}{n!} + \cdots .$$

$$\textbf{8.18}$$

The values of the derivatives $f^{(i)}(x_0, y_0)$ in (8.18) may be obtained by successive differentiation and evaluation at (x_0, y_0) of $f(x, y)$ under the assumption of this section. Any partial sum of the terms of the infinite series in the right-hand member of equation (8.18) represents an approximation to y_1.

Often, the higher-order derivatives of $f(x, y)$ which need to be determined involve considerable labor and time. In addition, it is necessary to consider the interval of convergence of the Taylor series expansion (8.17) of the solution function. The interval of convergence in many cases may be difficult to determine.

If the solution function does not have a Taylor series expansion, the method of this section cannot be employed.

EXAMPLE 1.   Use Taylor's series to find a numerical approximation to the particular solution at $x = 1$ of the differential equation $y' = y - x$ through $(0, 2)$.

Solution: Let $(x_0, y_0) = (0, 2)$. Then

$$
\begin{array}{ll}
f(x, y) = y - x, & f(0, 2) = 2, \\
f'(x, y) = y' - 1, & f'(0, 2) = 1, \\
f''(x, y) = y'', & f''(0, 2) = 1, \\
f'''(x, y) = y''', & f'''(0, 2) = 1, \\
f^{iv}(x, y) = y^{iv}, & f^{iv}(0, 2) = 1.
\end{array}
$$

Substituting in formula (8.18) with $\Delta x = 1$, the numerical approximation to y when $x = 1$ becomes

$$
y_1 = 2 + 2 + \frac{1}{2!} + \frac{1}{3!} + \frac{1}{4!} + \cdots,
$$

which may be written in the form

$$
y_1 = 2 + \left(1 + 1 + \frac{1}{2!} + \frac{1}{3!} + \frac{1}{4!} + \cdots\right).
$$

The infinite series within the parenthesis represents e. Hence, $y_1 = 2 + e = 4.718$, correct to the nearest thousandth of a unit. The student should compare the results of this example with the results of Example 1 in Section 8.3.

The particular solution of the differential equation of Example 1 with its initial condition is $y = e^x + x + 1$. This equation represents the closed form of the Taylor series solution

$$
y = 2 + 2x + \frac{x^2}{2!} + \frac{x^3}{3!} + \frac{x^4}{4!} + \cdots
$$

of the differential equation. It is not always possible to express the Taylor series solution of a differential equation in closed form. Whenever it is possible, then there exists some direct method of solution for obtaining the closed form.

EXAMPLE 2.   Show that Euler's method is a special case of the Taylor series method of solution of the differential equation $y' = f(x, y)$ satisfying the point (x_0, y_0).

Solution: Neglecting those terms in (8.18) containing second- and higher-order powers of Δx, the formula of the Taylor series method becomes

$$
y_1 = y_0 + f(x_0, y_0)\Delta x,
$$

which represents Euler's method of solution.

EXAMPLE 3.   Use Taylor's series to find an approximation to the particular solution at $x = 1.1$ of the differential equation $y' = 3x + y^2$ through $(1, 1)$.

Solution: Let $(x_0, y_0) = (1, 1)$. Then

$$f(x, y) = 3x + y^2, \qquad f(1, 1) = 3(1) + (1)^2 = 4,$$
$$f'(x, y) = 3 + 2yy', \qquad f'(1, 1) = 3 + 2(1)(4) = 11,$$
$$f''(x, y) = 2yy'' + 2(y')^2, \qquad f''(1, 1) = 2(1)(11) + 2(4)^2 = 54,$$
$$f'''(x, y) = 2yy''' + 6y'y'', \qquad f'''(1, 1) = 2(1)(54) + 6(4)(11) = 372,$$
$$f^{iv}(x, y) = 2yy^{iv} + 8y'y''' \qquad f^{iv}(1, 1) = 2(1)(372) + 8(4)(54)$$
$$+ 6(y'')^2, \qquad\qquad + 6(11)^2 = 3198,$$
$$\cdots \qquad\qquad\qquad \cdots$$

Substituting in formula (8.18) with $\Delta x = 0.1$, the numerical approximation to y when $x = 1.1$ becomes

$$y_1 = 1 + (0.1)(4) + \frac{(0.1)^2(11)}{2!} + \frac{(0.1)^3(54)}{3!} + \frac{(0.1)^4(372)}{4!} + \frac{(0.1)^5(3198)}{5!} + \cdots$$
$$= 1 + 0.4 + 0.055 + 0.009 + 0.00155 + 0.0002665 + \cdots$$
$$= 1.466,$$

correct to the nearest thousandth of a unit. Careful note should be made that 1.466 represents the sixth partial sum of the infinite Taylor series representing the exact solution.

The Taylor series method may be applied to the numerical solution of higher-order differential equations. Remember that, in such instances, n initial conditions must be imposed upon a differential equation of order n to obtain a particular solution.

EXAMPLE 4.   Use Taylor's series to find a numerical solution at $x = 0.5$ of the differential equation $y'' = xy$ given that $y' = 1$ and $y = 1$ when $x = 0$.

Solution: Since $x_0 = 0$, the Taylor series of (8.17) becomes a Maclaurin series (as in Example 1 of this section). Note that $f'(x, y)$ of (8.17) is equal to xy in this example. Now, $(x_0, y_0) = (0, 1)$ and $f(x_0, y_0) = 1$. Successive differentiation of both members of the given differential equation yields

$$y''' = f''(x, y) = xy' + y, \qquad f''(0, 1) = (0)(1) + 1 = 1,$$
$$y^{iv} = f'''(x, y) = xy'' + 2y', \qquad f'''(0, 1) = (0)(0) + 2(1) = 2,$$
$$y^{v} = f^{iv}(x, y) = xy''' + 3y'', \qquad f^{iv}(0, 1) = (0)(1) + 3(0) = 0,$$
$$y^{vi} = f^{v}(x, y) = xy^{iv} + 4y''', \qquad f^{v}(0, 1) = (0)(2) + 4(1) = 4,$$
$$\cdots \qquad\qquad\qquad \cdots$$

In general,

$$y^{(n)} = f^{(n-1)}(x, y) = xy^{(n-2)} + (n - 2)y^{(n-3)},$$
$$f^{(n-1)}(0, 1) = (n - 2)(n - 5)(n - 8) \ldots, \text{ for } n \geq 3,$$

where those factors which are negative are disregarded. The numerical approximation to y when $x = 0.5$ is given by formula (8.18) with $\Delta x = 0.5$. Hence,

$$y_1 = 1 + (0.5)(1) + \frac{(0.5)^3(1)}{3!} + \frac{(0.5)^4(2)}{4!} + \frac{(0.5)^6(4)}{6!} + \cdots$$

$$= 1 + 0.5 + 0.020833 + 0.0052083 + 0.000086805 + \cdots$$

$$= 1.526,$$

correct to the nearest thousandth of a unit using the fifth partial sum of the infinite Taylor series.

EXERCISES

In Exercises 1 through 4, find the first six terms of the Taylor series solution of the differential equation with the stated initial conditions. If possible, find the sum of the series in closed form.

1. $y' = x^2 - y^2$ through $(0, 1)$.
2. $y' = xy$ through $(0, 1)$.
3. $y' = y + \sin x$ through $\left(0, \dfrac{\pi}{2}\right)$.
4. $xy'' - (x + 2)y' + 2y = 0$ if $y' = 2$ and $y = 2$ when $x = 0$.

In Exercises 5 through 8, use the Taylor series method to find a numerical approximation to the particular solution of the differential equation with the stated initial conditions. Consider the approximation to the nearest thousandth of a unit using five terms of the series.

5. At $x = 0.1$ for $y' = 1 + xy^2$ through $(0, 1)$.
6. At $x = 0.2$ for $y' = 1 + y \sin x$ through $(0, 0)$.
7. At $x = 1.2$ for $y'' + y^2y' = x^3$ if $y' = 1$ and $y = 1$ when $x = 1$.
8. At $x = 0.2$ for $xy'' = y$ if $y' = 1$ and $y = 0$ when $x = 0$.
9. Use Taylor's series to show that

$$y_{n+1} = y_{n-1} + 2y_n'\Delta x$$

is a more accurate approximation to y_{n+1} than is

$$y_{n+1} = y_n + y_n'\Delta x$$

if Δx is sufficiently small. Discuss the conditions under which these approximations may be used.

10. Use Taylor's series to solve the system of simultaneous equations $y' = x + z$ and $z' = x + y$ given that $(x_0, y_0, z_0) = (0, 1, -1)$. If possible, express the solutions in closed form.

6. PICARD'S ITERATIVE METHOD

Iterative methods for the solution of a single ordinary equation and for systems of linear equations have been discussed. In this section, an iterative method of theoretical importance for the numerical solution of differential equations shall be presented.

Consider once more the first-order differential equation $y' = f(x, y)$ where $y = y_0$ when $x = x_0$. The particular solution of the differential equation may be expressed in the form

$$\int_{y_0}^{y} dy = \int_{x_0}^{x} f(x, y) \, dx, \qquad \qquad \textbf{8.19}$$

or in the form

$$y = y_0 + \int_{x_0}^{x} f(x, y) \, dx. \qquad \qquad \textbf{8.20}$$

Equation (8.20) is an example of an *integral equation*; that is, an equation in which the function y to be determined is stated explicitly in terms of an integral whose integrand contains the function y. Picard's method is an iterative method in which a sequence of functions $y_0(x)$, $y_1(x)$, $y_2(x)$, ... is obtained such that the limit of the sequence yields the particular solution function y. As $y_0(x)$, choose y_0. The next approximation function $y_1(x)$ is obtained by substituting $y_0(x)$ for y in the integrand of (8.20). Then

$$y_1(x) = y_0 + \int_{x_0}^{x} f(x, y_0(x)) \, dx. \qquad \qquad \textbf{8.21}$$

Since the integrand of (8.21) is a function of x alone, $y_1(x)$ may be determined providing the integration can be performed. In a similar manner, the next approximation function $y_2(x)$ may be obtained by substituting $y_1(x)$ for y in the integrand of (8.20); that is,

$$y_2(x) = y_0 + \int_{x_0}^{x} f(x, y_1(x)) \, dx. \qquad \qquad \textbf{8.22}$$

The process may be continued providing the integrations at each step are possible. The iterative process is described by the recursion formula

$$y_n(x) = y_0 + \int_{x_0}^{x} f(x, y_{n-1}(x)) \, dx \qquad \qquad \textbf{8.23}$$

and is known as *Picard's method*.

EXAMPLE 1.   Find a sequence of functions approximating the particular solution of the differential equation $y' = y$ through $(0, 1)$.

Solution: Now, $x_0 = 0$, $y_0 = 1$, and $f(x, y) = y$. Choosing $y_0(x) = y_0 = 1$ and using formula (8.23),

$$y_1(x) = 1 + \int_{0}^{x} (1) \, dx = 1 + x,$$

$$y_2(x) = 1 + \int_0^x (1 + x)\, dx = 1 + x + \frac{x^2}{2},$$

$$y_3(x) = 1 + \int_0^x \left(1 + x + \frac{x^2}{2}\right) dx = 1 + x + \frac{x^2}{2} + \frac{x^3}{3 \cdot 2},$$

$$y_4(x) = 1 + \int_0^x \left(1 + x + \frac{x^2}{2} + \frac{x^3}{3 \cdot 2}\right) dx = 1 + x + \frac{x^2}{2} + \frac{x^3}{3 \cdot 2} + \frac{x^4}{4 \cdot 3 \cdot 2},$$

$$\cdots$$

$$y_n(x) = 1 + x + \frac{x^2}{2!} + \frac{x^3}{3!} + \frac{x^4}{4!} + \cdots + \frac{x^n}{n!}.$$

Note that $y_n(x)$ represents the nth partial sum of the Taylor series expansion of e^x which is the exact solution of the given differential equation with its initial condition; that is,

$$\lim_{n \to \infty} y_n(x) = e^x.$$

EXAMPLE 2. Use Picard's method to determine an approximation to the particular solution at $x = 0.2$ of the differential equation $y' = 1 + y^2$ through $(0, 0)$. Consider the approximation to the nearest thousandth of a unit.

Solution: Now, $x_0 = 0$, $y_0 = 0$, and $f(x, y) = 1 + y^2$. As $y_0(x)$, choose y_0; that is, 0. Using the recursion formula (8.23), it follows that

$$y_1(x) = \int_0^x dx = x, \qquad\qquad\qquad y_1(0.2) = 0.2,$$

$$y_2(x) = \int_0^x (1 + x^2)\, dx = x + \frac{x^3}{3}, \qquad\qquad y_2(0.2) = 0.203,$$

$$y_3(x) = \int_0^x \left[1 + \left(x + \frac{x^3}{3}\right)^2\right] dx = x + \frac{x^3}{3} + \frac{2x^5}{15} + \frac{x^7}{63}, \quad y_3(0.2) = 0.203.$$

Since $y_2(0.2)$ and $y_3(0.2)$ agree to the nearest thousandth of a unit, the process is terminated and 0.203 is accepted as a numerical approximation to y when $x = 0.2$ under the initial condition.

Example 1 illustrated how a sequence of approximation functions obtained by Picard's method may converge to a particular solution function of a differential equation with initial conditions. In Example 2, a sequence of values was determined. However, it should be remembered that these values represented the evaluation of partial sums of an infinite series. Therefore, the question of convergence of the sequence of values needs to be considered carefully. As an illustration of the difficulties involved, consider Example 2 again. It can be shown that since $\sec^2 x = 1 + \tan^2 x$, the exact particular solution of the given differential equation with its initial condition is $y = \tan x$ providing $-\dfrac{\pi}{2} < x < \dfrac{\pi}{2}$.

Hence, Picard's method would not converge to a particular numerical solution for values of x outside this interval. Furthermore, for values of x where $|x|$ is close to $\frac{\pi}{2}$, a sequence of numerical values obtained by Picard's method would converge too slowly for the method to be considered practical in this problem.

Picard's method may also be used to approximate particular solutions of higher-order differential equations and systems of differential equations. Example 3 illustrates the application of the method to the numerical solution of a second-order differential equation.

EXAMPLE 3.   Use Picard's method to approximate the particular solution at $x = 0.1$ of the differential equation $y'' = 4y - 2xy'$ if $y' = 0.5$ and $y = 0.2$ when $x = 0$. Consider the approximation to the nearest thousandth of a unit.

Solution: The second-order differential equation $y'' = 4y - 2xy'$ is equivalent to the system of two simultaneous differential equations

$$\begin{cases} y' = z, \\ z' = 4y - 2xz, \end{cases}$$

where $(x_0, y_0, z_0) = (0, 0.2, 0.5)$. Now, using Picard's method, the recursion formulas which will be used simultaneously to solve both first-order differential equations are

$$y_n(x) = 0.2 + \int_0^x z_{n-1}(x) \, dx,$$

and

$$z_n(x) = 0.5 + \int_0^x (4y_{n-1}(x) - 2xz_{n-1}(x)) \, dx.$$

Choosing $y_0(x) = 0.2$ and $z_0(x) = 0.5$, then

$$y_1(x) = 0.2 + \int_0^x (0.5) \, dx$$

$$= 0.2 + 0.5x,$$

$$y_1(0.1) = 0.25,$$

$$z_1(x) = 0.5 + \int_0^x [4(0.2) - 2(0.5)x] \, dx$$

$$= 0.5 + 0.8x - 0.5x^2,$$

$$z_1(0.1) = 0.575,$$

$$y_2(x) = 0.2 + \int_0^x (0.5 + 0.8x - 0.5x^2) \, dx$$

$$= 0.2 + 0.5x + 0.4x^2 - 0.167x^3,$$

$$y_2(0.1) = 0.254,$$

$$z_2(x) = 0.5 + \int_0^x [4(0.2 + 0.5x) - 2x(0.5 + 0.8x - 0.5x^2)]\, dx$$

$$= 0.5 + \int_0^x (0.8 + x - 1.6x^2 + x^3)\, dx$$

$$= 0.5 + 0.8x + 0.5x^2 - 0.533x^3 + 0.25x^4,$$

$$z_2(0.1) = 0.584,$$

$$y_3(x) = 0.2 + \int_0^x (0.5 + 0.8x + 0.5x^2 - 0.533x^3 + 0.25x^4)\, dx$$

$$= 0.2 + 0.5x + 0.4x^2 + 0.167x^3 - 0.133x^4 + 0.05x^5,$$

$$y_3(0.1) = 0.254.$$

Since $y_2(0.1)$ and $y_3(0.1)$ agree to the nearest thousandth of a unit, the process is terminated and 0.254 is accepted as a numerical approximation to y when $x = 0.1$ under the initial conditions. This result agrees reasonably well with the results of Example 3 of Section 8.3.

EXERCISES

In Exercises 1 through 4, use Picard's method to find $y_4(x)$ as an approximation to the particular solution of the differential equation with the stated initial conditions.

1. $y' = x - y$ through $(0, 1)$.
2. $y' = x + y + 1$ through $(0, 0)$.
3. $y' = 1 + xy$ through $(0, 1)$.
4. $y'' = x - y^2$ if $y' = 2$ and $y = 1$ when $x = 0$.

   In Exercises 5 and 6, use Picard's method to find a numerical approximation to the particular solution of the differential equation with the stated initial conditions. Consider the approximation to the nearest thousandth of a unit.

5. At $x = 0.4$ for $y' = 2x - y + 2$ through $(0, 1)$. Compare the approximation with the results of Example 2 of Section 8.3.
6. At $x = 0.5$ for $y'' = xy$ if $y' = 1$ and $y = 1$ when $x = 0$. Compare the approximation with the results of Example 4 of Section 8.5.
7. Discuss why the particular solution of the differential equation $y' = \sin x + \cos y$ with initial condition $y = 0$ when $x = 0$ cannot be approximated by Picard's method.

7. THE RUNGE-KUTTA METHOD

The method to be presented in this section was developed by C. Runge in 1894 and improved upon in 1901 by W. Kutta. The *Runge-Kutta method* of solution is based upon the concept of Simpson's Rule of numerical integration.

Let

$$y_0, \quad y_0 + \frac{\Delta y}{2}, \quad \text{and} \quad y_1$$

be the values of the dependent variable corresponding to the values

$$x_0, \quad x_0 + \frac{\Delta x}{2}, \quad \text{and} \quad x_0 + \Delta x$$

of the independent variable on the integral curve of $y' = f(x, y)$ through (x_0, y_0). Then since

$$y_1 = y_0 + \int_{x_0}^{x_0 + \Delta x} f(x, y) \, dx,$$

using Simpson's Rule, an approximation to y_1 is given by the expression

$$y_1 = y_0 + \frac{\Delta x}{6}\left[f(x_0, y_0) + 4f\left(x_0 + \frac{\Delta x}{2}, y_0 + \frac{\Delta y}{2}\right) + f(x_0 + \Delta x, y_0 + \Delta y)\right].$$

$$\textbf{8.24}$$

Now, only y_0 is known and approximations need to be obtained for $y_0 + \dfrac{\Delta y}{2}$ and $y_0 + \Delta y$ in the right-hand member of equation (8.24) in order to approximate $f\left(x_0 + \dfrac{\Delta x}{2}, y_0 + \dfrac{\Delta y}{2}\right)$ and $f(x_0 + \Delta x, y_0 + \Delta y)$. A first approximation to $y_0 + \dfrac{\Delta y}{2}$ is made by considering the change in y along the tangent line to the integral curve at (x_0, y_0); that is,

$$y_0 + \frac{\Delta y}{2} = y_0 + \frac{f(x_0, y_0)\,\Delta x}{2},$$

or

$$y_0 + \frac{\Delta y}{2} = y_0 + \frac{k_1}{2}, \qquad \textbf{8.25}$$

where

$$k_1 = f(x_0, y_0)\,\Delta x. \qquad \textbf{8.26}$$

A second approximation to $y_0 + \dfrac{\Delta y}{2}$ is made by considering the change in y along the line through (x_0, y_0) with slope $f\left(x_0 + \dfrac{\Delta x}{2}, y_0 + \dfrac{k_1}{2}\right)$; that is,

$$y_0 + \frac{\Delta y}{2} = y_0 + \frac{f\left(x_0 + \dfrac{\Delta x}{2}, y_0 + \dfrac{k_1}{2}\right)\Delta x}{2},$$

or

$$y_0 + \frac{\Delta y}{2} = y_0 + \frac{k_2}{2}, \qquad \textbf{8.27}$$

where

$$k_2 = f\left(x_0 + \frac{\Delta x}{2}, y_0 + \frac{k_1}{2}\right) \Delta x. \qquad \textbf{8.28}$$

An approximation to $y_0 + \Delta y$ is made by considering the change in y along the line through (x_0, y_0) with slope $f\left(x_0 + \frac{\Delta x}{2}, y_0 + \frac{k_2}{2}\right)$; that is,

$$y_0 + \Delta y = y_0 + f\left(x_0 + \frac{\Delta x}{2}, y_0 + \frac{k_2}{2}\right) \Delta x,$$

or

$$y_0 + \Delta y = y_0 + k_3, \qquad \textbf{8.29}$$

where

$$k_3 = f\left(x_0 + \frac{\Delta x}{2}, y_0 + \frac{k_2}{2}\right) \Delta x. \qquad \textbf{8.30}$$

Now, equation (8.24) may be written in the form

$$y_1 = y_0 + \tfrac{1}{6}(k_1 + 2k_2 + 2k_3 + k_4), \qquad \textbf{8.31}$$

where

$$k_4 = f(x_0 + \Delta x, y_0 + k_3) \Delta x. \qquad \textbf{8.32}$$

Note that the sum of the expressions for k_2 and k_3 in (8.28) and (8.30), respectively, each with equal weighting factors 2, were used to approximate

$$4f\left(x_0 + \frac{\Delta x}{2}, y_0 + \frac{\Delta y}{2}\right) \Delta x.$$

Essentially, Δy has been approximated by considering a weighted average of the approximations for $f(x, y)$ at the beginning, mid-point, and end of the interval from x_0 to $x_0 + \Delta x$. In summary, the Runge-Kutta method for approximating y_1 given $y' = f(x, y)$ through (x_0, y_0) is given by the set of formulas (8.33):

$$y_1 = y_0 + \tfrac{1}{6}(k_1 + 2k_2 + 2k_3 + k_4),$$

where

$$k_1 = f(x_0, y_0) \Delta x,$$

$$k_2 = f\left(x_0 + \frac{\Delta x}{2}, y_0 + \frac{k_1}{2}\right) \Delta x,$$

$$k_3 = f\left(x_0 + \frac{\Delta x}{2}, y_0 + \frac{k_2}{2}\right) \Delta x, \qquad \textbf{8.33}$$

$$k_4 = f(x_0 + \Delta x, y_0 + k_3) \Delta x.$$

EXAMPLE 1.   Use the Runge-Kutta method to find a numerical approximation to the particular solution at $x = 0.5$ of the differential equation $y' = x + y^2$ through $(0, 0)$.

Solution: Now, $(x_0, y_0) = (0, 0)$, $f(x, y) = x + y^2$, and $\Delta x = 0.5$. Then, using the formulas of (8.33),

$$k_1 = f(0, 0)(0.5) = (0 + 0^2)(0.5) = 0,$$
$$k_2 = f(0.25, 0)(0.5) = (0.25 + 0^2)(0.5) = 0.125,$$
$$k_3 = f(0.25, 0.0625)(0.5) = [0.25 + (0.0625)^2](0.5) = 0.127,$$
$$k_4 = f(0.5, 0.127)(0.5) = [0.5 + (0.127)^2](0.5) = 0.258.$$

Hence,

$$y_1 = \tfrac{1}{6}[0 + 2(0.125) + 2(0.127) + 0.258]$$
$$= \tfrac{1}{6}(0.762)$$
$$= 0.127.$$

EXAMPLE 2.   Use the Runge-Kutta method to approximate the particular solution at $x = 1$ of the differential equation $y' = xy$ through $(0, 1)$.

Solution: Now, $(x_0, y_0) = (0, 1)$ and $f(x, y) = xy$. Since $\Delta x = 1$,

$$k_1 = f(0, 1) = (0)(1) = 0,$$
$$k_2 = f(0.5, 1) = (0.5)(1) = 0.5,$$
$$k_3 = f(0.5, 1.25) = (0.5)(1.25) = 0.625,$$
$$k_4 = f(1, 1.625) = (1)(1.625) = 1.625.$$

Hence,

$$y_1 = 1 + \tfrac{1}{6}[0 + 2(0.5) + 2(0.625) + 1.625]$$
$$= 1 + \tfrac{1}{6}(3.875)$$
$$= 1.646,$$

correct to the nearest thousandth of a unit. The exact solution to the differential equation with the initial condition is $y = e^{x^2/2}$. When $x = 1$, $y = 1.649$, correct to the nearest thousandth of a unit.

EXAMPLE 3.   Show that the Runge-Kutta method for calculating Δy given $y' = f(x, y)$ through (x_0, y_0) becomes Simpson's Rule if $f(x, y)$ is a function of x only.

Solution: Using the formulas of (8.33) with $f(x, y) = g(x)$,

$$k_1 = g(x_0)\, \Delta x,$$
$$k_2 = g\left(x_0 + \frac{\Delta x}{2}\right) \Delta x,$$
$$k_3 = g\left(x_0 + \frac{\Delta x}{2}\right) \Delta x,$$
$$k_4 = g(x_0 + \Delta x)\, \Delta x.$$

Then

$$\Delta y = \frac{1}{6}\left[g(x_0)\,\Delta x + 2g\left(x_0 + \frac{\Delta x}{2}\right)\Delta x + 2g\left(x_0 + \frac{\Delta x}{2}\right)\Delta x + g(x_0 + \Delta x)\,\Delta x\right]$$

$$= \frac{\left(\frac{\Delta x}{2}\right)}{3}\left[g(x_0) + 4g\left(x_0 + \frac{\Delta x}{2}\right) + g(x_0 + \Delta x)\right],$$

which is Simpson's Rule for the numerical integration of $g(x)$ over the interval x_0 to $x_0 + \Delta x$.

EXAMPLE 4. Use the Runge-Kutta method to approximate the particular solution at $x = 2$ of the differential equation $y'' = x + yy'$ if $y' = 0$ and $y = 1$ when $x = 0$.

Solution: The second-order differential equation $y'' = x + yy'$ is equivalent to the system of two simultaneous differential equations

$$\begin{cases} y' = z, \\ z' = x + yz, \end{cases}$$

where $(x_0, y_0, z_0) = (0, 1, 0)$. Let $f(x, y, z) = z$ and $g(x, y, z) = x + yz$. Then

$$y_1 = y_0 + \tfrac{1}{6}(k_1 + 2k_2 + 2k_3 + k_4),$$

where

$$k_1 = f(x_0, y_0, z_0)\,\Delta x,$$

$$k_2 = f\left(x_0 + \frac{\Delta x}{2}, y_0 + \frac{k_1}{2}, z_0 + \frac{m_1}{2}\right)\Delta x,$$

$$k_3 = f\left(x_0 + \frac{\Delta x}{2}, y_0 + \frac{k_2}{2}, z_0 + \frac{m_2}{2}\right)\Delta x,$$

$$k_4 = f(x_0 + \Delta x, y_0 + k_3, z_0 + m_3)\,\Delta x;$$

and

$$z_1 = z_0 + \tfrac{1}{6}(m_1 + 2m_2 + 2m_3 + m_4),$$

where

$$m_1 = g(x_0, y_0, z_0)\,\Delta x,$$

$$m_2 = g\left(x_0 + \frac{\Delta x}{2}, y_0 + \frac{k_1}{2}, z_0 + \frac{m_1}{2}\right)\Delta x,$$

$$m_3 = g\left(x_0 + \frac{\Delta x}{2}, y_0 + \frac{k_2}{2}, z_0 + \frac{m_2}{2}\right)\Delta x,$$

$$m_4 = g(x + \Delta x, y_0 + k_3, z_0 + m_3)\,\Delta x.$$

Therefore, since $\Delta x = 2$,

$$k_1 = 2f(0, 1, 0) = (2)(0) = 0,$$
$$m_1 = 2g(0, 1, 0) = (2)[(0) + (1)(0)] = 0,$$
$$k_2 = 2f(1, 1, 0) = 2(0) = 0,$$
$$m_2 = 2g(1, 1, 0) = 2[(1) + (1)(0)] = 2,$$
$$k_3 = 2f(1, 1, 1) = 2(1) = 2,$$
$$m_3 = 2g(1, 1, 1) = 2[(1) + (1)(1)] = 4,$$
$$k_4 = 2f(2, 3, 4) = 2(4) = 8.$$

Hence,

$$y_1 = 1 + \tfrac{1}{6}[0 + 2(0) + 2(2) + 8]$$
$$= 1 + \tfrac{1}{6}(12)$$
$$= 3.$$

EXERCISES

In Exercises 1 through 6, use the Runge-Kutta method to find numerical approximations to the particular solutions of the differential equation with the stated initial conditions. Find the approximations to the nearest thousandth of a unit.

1. At $x = 0.4$ for $y' = 2x - y + 2$ through $(0, 1)$. Compare the approximation with the results of the Example of Section 8.4 and the exact results.

2. At $x = 1.2$ for $y' = x + y$ through $(1, 0)$.

3. At $x = 0.1$ for $y' = 3x + y^2$ through $(0, 1)$.

4. At $x = 2$ for $y' = \sqrt{x + y}$ through $(1, 3)$.

5. Over the interval $0 \leq x \leq 1$ for $y' = y - x$ through $(0, 2)$. Let $\Delta x = 0.1$. Compare the approximations with the results of Example 1 of Section 8.3 and the exact results.

6. At $x = 0.1$ for $y'' = 4y - 2xy'$ if $y' = 0.5$ and $y = 0.2$ when $x = 0$.

Appendix—Determinants

A brief discussion of determinants is presented here for those readers whose mathematical backgrounds do not include the study of determinants. This presentation is not meant to be a complete, rigorous development of the theory of determinants. It will, however, be sufficient to enable the reader to understand the use of determinants in the body of this book.

A *determinant of order two* is a square array of elements a_{ij} of the form

$$\begin{vmatrix} a_{11} & a_{12} \\ a_{21} & a_{22} \end{vmatrix}$$

whose value is $a_{11}a_{22} - a_{12}a_{21}$. A *determinant of order three* is a square array of elements a_{ij} of the form

$$\begin{vmatrix} a_{11} & a_{12} & a_{13} \\ a_{21} & a_{22} & a_{23} \\ a_{31} & a_{32} & a_{33} \end{vmatrix}$$

whose value is

$$a_{11}a_{22}a_{33} + a_{12}a_{23}a_{31} + a_{13}a_{21}a_{32} - a_{13}a_{22}a_{31} - a_{11}a_{23}a_{32} - a_{12}a_{21}a_{33}.$$

In general, a *determinant of order n* is a square array of n^2 elements a_{ij} of the form

$$\begin{vmatrix} a_{11} & a_{12} & \cdots & a_{1n} \\ a_{21} & a_{22} & \cdots & a_{2n} \\ \cdot & & & \\ \cdot & & & \\ \cdot & & & \\ a_{n1} & a_{n2} & \cdots & a_{nn} \end{vmatrix}$$

whose value is $\Sigma (-1)^k a_{1i_1} a_{2i_2} a_{3i_3} \cdots a_{nin}$, where the second subscripts $i_1, i_2, i_3, \ldots, i_n$ are equal to $1, 2, 3, \ldots, n$ in some order; that is, the second subscripts are chosen such that each column number is represented once, and only once, in each term of the sum. The exponent k represents the number of *permutations* (interchanges) of two elements necessary for the second subscripts to be placed in the order 1, 2, 3, ..., n. For example, in the term containing

$$a_{13}a_{21}a_{34}a_{42}$$

in the expansion of a fourth-order determinant, the value of k is three since three permutations of two elements are necessary for the second subscripts to be placed in the order 1, 2, 3, 4:

$$a_{13}a_{21}a_{34}a_{42} = a_{21}a_{13}a_{34}a_{42} = a_{21}a_{13}a_{42}a_{34} = a_{21}a_{42}a_{13}a_{34}.$$

Hence, the term containing $a_{13}a_{21}a_{34}a_{42}$ has associated with it the factor $(-1)^3$; that is, -1. The value of a determinant of order $n \geq 4$ is seldom obtained by use of the definition. Instead, a sequence of theorems are usually employed which make the computation less laborious.

The following theorems which are stated and illustrated for determinants of the third-order are valid for nth-order determinants. The reader should verify each of these theorems for a third-order determinant to fix in mind the statement of the theorem.

Theorem I. *The value of a determinant remains unchanged if the rows and columns are interchanged; that is,*

$$\begin{vmatrix} a_{11} & a_{12} & a_{13} \\ a_{21} & a_{22} & a_{23} \\ a_{31} & a_{32} & a_{33} \end{vmatrix} = \begin{vmatrix} a_{11} & a_{21} & a_{31} \\ a_{12} & a_{22} & a_{32} \\ a_{13} & a_{23} & a_{33} \end{vmatrix}.$$

As a result of Theorem 1, every theorem which follows and is a statement concerning the rows of a determinant has a corollary which concerns the columns of the determinant.

Theorem 2. *The value of a determinant is changed by a factor* (-1) *if any two rows are interchanged; that is, for example,*

$$\begin{vmatrix} a_{11} & a_{12} & a_{13} \\ a_{21} & a_{22} & a_{23} \\ a_{31} & a_{32} & a_{33} \end{vmatrix} = - \begin{vmatrix} a_{31} & a_{32} & a_{33} \\ a_{21} & a_{22} & a_{23} \\ a_{11} & a_{12} & a_{13} \end{vmatrix}.$$

Theorem 3. *The value of a determinant is changed by a factor k if all the elements of any row are changed by a factor k;* that is, for example,

$$
k \begin{vmatrix} a_{11} & a_{12} & a_{13} \\ a_{21} & a_{22} & a_{23} \\ a_{31} & a_{32} & a_{33} \end{vmatrix} = \begin{vmatrix} a_{11} & a_{12} & a_{13} \\ a_{21} & a_{22} & a_{23} \\ ka_{31} & ka_{32} & ka_{33} \end{vmatrix}.
$$

Theorem 4. *The value of a determinant remains unchanged if the same multiple of the elements of a row is added to the corresponding elements of another row;* that is, for example,

$$
\begin{vmatrix} a_{11} & a_{12} & a_{13} \\ a_{21} & a_{22} & a_{23} \\ a_{31} & a_{32} & a_{33} \end{vmatrix} = \begin{vmatrix} a_{11} & a_{12} & a_{13} \\ a_{21}+ka_{11} & a_{22}+ka_{12} & a_{23}+ka_{13} \\ a_{31} & a_{32} & a_{33} \end{vmatrix}.
$$

The *cofactor* of any element a_{ij} in a determinant D is defined as the product of $(-1)^{i+j}$ and the determinant obtained by eliminating the elements of the ith row and the jth column of D. For example, the cofactor of a_{23} in

$$
\begin{vmatrix} a_{11} & a_{12} & a_{13} \\ a_{21} & a_{22} & a_{23} \\ a_{31} & a_{32} & a_{33} \end{vmatrix} \text{ is equal to } (-1)^{2+3} \begin{vmatrix} a_{11} & a_{12} \\ a_{31} & a_{32} \end{vmatrix}.
$$

Theorem 5. *The value of a determinant is equal to the sum of the products of the elements of a row by their cofactors;* that is, for example,

$$
\begin{vmatrix} a_{11} & a_{12} & a_{13} \\ a_{21} & a_{22} & a_{23} \\ a_{31} & a_{32} & a_{33} \end{vmatrix} = a_{11} \begin{vmatrix} a_{22} & a_{23} \\ a_{32} & a_{33} \end{vmatrix} - a_{12} \begin{vmatrix} a_{21} & a_{23} \\ a_{31} & a_{33} \end{vmatrix}
$$

$$
+ a_{13} \begin{vmatrix} a_{21} & a_{22} \\ a_{31} & a_{32} \end{vmatrix}.
$$

ANSWERS

Chapter 1

SECTION 2   **Page 5**

4. $\Delta^5 y_0 = y_5 - 5y_4 + 10y_3 - 10y_2 + 5y_1 - y_0.$

5. $\Delta^n y_k = \sum_{i=0}^{n} (-1)^i \binom{n}{i} y_{n+k-i}.$

6. **(a)** 84;   **(b)** 125;   **(c)** 602;   **(d)** 593;   **(e)** 114.

7. $-3.$

SECTION 3   **Page 9**

1. **(a)** $3x^2 + 3x + 1$;   **(b)** $6a$;   **(c)** $a^x(a - 1)$;   **(d)** $a^x(a - 1)^n$;

   (e) $e^x(e - 1)$;   **(f)** $\binom{x}{2}$;   **(g)** $xx!$;

   (h) $0.84147 \cos x - 0.45970 \sin x$;   **(i)** $\dfrac{-3}{(x + 1)(x + 2)(x + 3)(x + 4)}$;

   (j) $(2x + 3)3^x$;   **(k)** $x^4 + 4x^3 + 6x^2 + 4x + 1$;   **(l)** $(x + 2)!$;

   (m) $0.54030 \cos x - 0.84147 \sin x$;   **(n)** $\binom{x + 1}{r}$;

   (o) $\dfrac{1}{(x + 1)(x + 2)}$;   **(p)** e^{x+n};   **(q)** $2x - 1$;

   (r) $\dfrac{-3}{(x - 1)(x)(x + 1)(x + 2)}$;   **(s)** $3x^2 - 6x + 3$;   **(t)** $x - n.$

2. $8a.$

3. 1019.

4. $ax^2 + (6a + b)x + (9a + 3b + c)$.

5. $\begin{pmatrix} x \\ r - k \end{pmatrix}$.

8. 2223.

9. -1.

10. $y_i = y_2 + \begin{pmatrix} i - 2 \\ 1 \end{pmatrix} \Delta y_2 + \begin{pmatrix} i - 2 \\ 2 \end{pmatrix} \Delta^2 y_2 + \cdots + \begin{pmatrix} i - 2 \\ n \end{pmatrix} \Delta^n y_2 + \cdots$.

12. **(a)** 3;   **(b)** 19;   **(c)** 1.

SECTION 5   Page 15

4. $h^n n!$.

5. $a_0 h^n n!$.

8. Degree one.

9. $a^2 b^3 h^6 6!$.

10. **(a)** $\frac{1}{2}x^2 - \frac{1}{2}x + k$, where k is any real number;

   (b) $\frac{1}{2}x^2 + \frac{5}{2}x + k$, where k is any real number;

   (c) $\frac{2}{3}x^3 - \frac{5}{2}x^2 + \frac{35}{6}x + k$, where k is any real number.

11. **(a)** $y_2 = -9$;   **(b)** $y_5 = 75$;   **(c)** $y_2 = 14$.

Chapter 2

SECTION 2   Page 19

2. **(a)** $x^4 - x^3 - x^2 - x + 5$;   **(b)** $x^2 - 3x + 1$;   **(c)** $x^3 - 4x + 3$;

   (d) $x^3 - 11x^2 + 42x - 58$;   **(e)** $125x^3 - 15x$.

3. 0.5447.

4. 2.4484.

5. $I(x) = y_0 + \begin{pmatrix} x - 2 \\ 1 \end{pmatrix} \Delta y_0 + \begin{pmatrix} x - 2 \\ 2 \end{pmatrix} \Delta^2 y_0 + \cdots + \begin{pmatrix} x - 2 \\ n \end{pmatrix} \Delta^n y_0$.

6. $I(x) = y_0 + \dfrac{(x - x_0)\,\Delta y_0}{h} + \dfrac{(x - x_0)(x - x_0 - h)\,\Delta^2 y_0}{2!\,h^2}$

$\qquad + \dfrac{(x - x_0)(x - x_0 - h)(x - x_0 - 2h)\,\Delta^3 y_0}{3!\,h^3} + \cdots .$

SECTION 3   Page 22

1. **(a)** $x^2 - 3x + 5;$ **(b)** $-4x^2 + 6x + 10;$ **(c)** $x^3 - 2x^2 - 4x + 5;$

    (d) $x^2 + 5;$ **(e)** $-\frac{1}{72}x^3 + \frac{29}{72}x^2 + \frac{5}{4}x + 11.$

2. 0.6026.

4. $\dfrac{y_0}{24},\ -\dfrac{y_1}{6},\ \dfrac{y_2}{4},\ -\dfrac{y_3}{6},\ \dfrac{y_4}{24}.$

5. 1.3125.

SECTION 5   Page 31

3. **(a)** $3x^2 - 4x + 10;$ **(b)** $x^3 - x;$ **(c)** $x^4 - 7x + 1;$ **(d)** $4x + 2.$

4. $\frac{227}{20}.$

5. 8.49.

6. $y_3 = \frac{43}{2}.$

7. $y_1 = \frac{37}{4};\ y_3 = \frac{65}{4}.$

8. $x^2 - 3x + 6.$

11. $y = \dfrac{4 - 2x}{1 + x}.$

SECTION 6   Page 36

1. $x^4 - 6x^3 + 9x^2 + 8x + 1.$

3. $y = y_0 + x\,\Delta y_{-1} + \dbinom{x + 1}{2}\Delta^2 y_{-2} + \dbinom{x + 2}{3}\Delta^3 y_{-3}$

$\qquad + \dbinom{x + 3}{4}\Delta^4 y_{-4} + \dbinom{x + 4}{5}\Delta^5 y_{-5} + \cdots .$

4. $y = y_0 + \dfrac{x}{2}(\Delta y_0 + \Delta y_{-1}) + \dfrac{x^2}{2!}\Delta^2 y_{-1} + \dfrac{x(x^2 - 1)}{2 \cdot 3!}(\Delta^3 y_{-1} + \Delta^3 y_{-2})$

$\qquad + \dfrac{x^2(x^2 - 1)}{4!}\Delta^4 y_{-2} + \dfrac{x(x^2 - 1)(x^2 - 4)}{2 \cdot 5!}(\Delta^5 y_{-2} + \Delta^5 y_{-3}) + \cdots .$

5. $y = \frac{1}{2}(y_0 + y_1) + \left(\dfrac{2x-1}{2}\right)\Delta y_0 + \dfrac{x(x-1)}{2\cdot 2!}\,(\Delta^2 y_{-1} + \Delta^2 y_0)$

$\qquad + \dfrac{(2x-1)(x)(x-1)}{2\cdot 3!}\,\Delta^3 y_{-1}$

$\qquad + \dfrac{(x+1)(x)(x-1)(x-2)}{2\cdot 4!}\,(\Delta^4 y_{-1} + \Delta^4 y_{-2})$

$\qquad + \dfrac{(2x-1)(x+1)(x)(x-1)(x-2)}{2\cdot 5!}\,\Delta^5 y_{-2} + \cdots.$

6. $x^4 - x^2 + x + 1.$

7. **(a)** $I(x) = 6x^2 - 5x + 1,\ I(-2.5) = 51,\ I(-1) = 12,\ I(-0.5) = 5,$
$\qquad I(0) = 1,\ I(0.5) = 0,\ I(1) = 2,\ I(2.5) = 26;$

   (b) $I(x) = 6x^2 + 7x + 1,\ I(-2.5) = 21,\ I(-1) = 0,\ I(-0.5) = -1,$
$\qquad I(0) = 1,\ I(0.5) = 6,\ I(1) = 14,\ I(2.5) = 56;$

   (c) $I(x) = x + 1,\ I(-2.5) = -1.5,\ I(-1) = 0,\ I(-0.5) = 0.5,\ I(0) = 1,$
$\qquad I(0.5) = 1.5,\ I(1) = 2,\ I(2.5) = 3.5;$

   (d) $I(x) = x + 1,\ I(-2.5) = -1.5,\ I(-1) = 0,\ I(-0.5) = 0.5,\ I(0) = 1,$
$\qquad I(0.5) = 1.5,\ I(1) = 2,\ I(2.5) = 3.5;$

   (e) $I(x) = x + 1,\ I(-2.5) = -1.5,\ I(-1) = 0,\ I(-0.5) = 0.5,\ I(0) = 1,$
$\qquad I(0.5) = 1.5,\ I(1) = 2,\ I(2.5) = 3.5;$

   (f) $I(x) = \frac{3}{2}x^2 - \frac{1}{2}x + 1,\ I(-2.5) = 11.625,\ I(-1) = 3,\ I(-0.5) = 1.625,$
$\qquad I(0) = 1,\ I(0.5) = 1.125,\ I(1) = 2,\ I(2.5) = 9.125.$

10. 6.

SECTION 7   Page 42

1.

x \ y	0		1		2		3
0	0	(1)	1	(1)	2	(1)	3
	(1)		(0)		(−1)		(−2)
1	1	(0)	1	(0)	1	(0)	1
	(3)		(2)		(1)		(0)
2	4	(−1)	3	(−1)	2	(−1)	1

2.

x \ y	0		1		2		3
-1	-3	(-3)	-6	(-3)	-9	(-3)	-12
		(3)		(4)		(5)	(6)
0	0	(-2)	-2	(-2)	-4	(-2)	-6
		(3)		(4)		(5)	(6)
1	3	(-1)	2	(-1)	1	(-1)	0
		(3)		(4)		(5)	(6)
2	6	(0)	6	(0)	6	(0)	6
		(3)		(4)		(5)	(6)
3	9	(1)	10	(1)	11	(1)	12

3. $z_{32} - 3z_{22} + 3z_{12} - z_{02} - 2z_{31} + 6z_{21}$

$\qquad - 6z_{11} + 2z_{01} + z_{30} - 3z_{20} + 3z_{10} - z_{00}.$

4. $z = x + xy.$

5. $z = x^2 - y + 3.$

6. 29.

7. $z = -2xy^2.$

Chapter 3

SECTION 2   Page 47

3. $x^7 - 21x^6 + 175x^5 - 735x^4 + 1624x^3 - 1764x^2 + 720x.$

4. $x^6 - 15x^5 + 85x^4 - 225x^3 + 274x^2 - 120x.$

5. $S_1^9 = 40320,\ S_2^9 = -109584,\ S_3^9 = 118124,\ S_4^9 = -67284,\ S_5^9 = 22449,$

$S_6^9 = -4536,\ S_7^9 = 546,\ S_8^9 = -36,\ S_9^9 = 1;$

$S_1^{10} = -362880,\ S_2^{10} = 1026576,\ S_3^{10} = -1172700,\ S_4^{10} = 723680,$

$S_5^{10} = -269325,\ S_6^{10} = 63273,\ S_7^{10} = -9450,\ S_8^{10} = 870,\ S_9^{10} = -45,$

$S_{10}^{10} = 1.$

6. $-\frac{1}{6} + \frac{137}{180}x - \frac{15}{16}x^2 + \frac{17}{36}x^3 - \frac{5}{48}x^4 + \frac{1}{120}x^5.$

7. $3x^2.$

SECTION 3   Page 51

1. $6x^2 - 6x + 4.$

2. $4x^3.$

3. $20x^3 + 60x^2 + 64x + 24.$

5. $D^2 = \frac{1}{h^2} [\Delta^2 - \Delta^3 + \frac{11}{12}\Delta^4 - \frac{5}{6}\Delta^5 + \cdots];$

$D^3 = \frac{1}{h^3} [\Delta^3 - \frac{3}{2}\Delta^4 + \frac{7}{4}\Delta^5 - \frac{15}{8}\Delta^6 + \cdots].$

6. $\Delta = hD + \dfrac{h^2 D^2}{2!} + \dfrac{h^3 D^3}{3!} + \cdots + \dfrac{h^n D^n}{n!} + \cdots.$

7. $e^x(e^h - 1).$

SECTION 8   Page 58

2. 0.45932 by the trapezoidal rule with relative error 0.00083; 0.45970 by Simpson's Rule, correct to the nearest hundred-thousandth of a unit.

3. 0.693772 by the trapezoidal rule with relative error 0.00089; 0.69315 by Simpson's Rule correct to the nearest hundred-thousandth of a unit.

4. 40,302 by the three-eighths rule with relative error 0.00778; 39,996 by Weddle's Rule with relative error 0.00013.

5. $\int_0^6 y\,dx = -166,$ $\int_6^{12} y\,dx = 1328,$ and $\int_0^{12} y\,dx = 1162$ by the trapezoidal rule; $\int_0^6 y\,dx = -168,$ $\int_6^{12} y\,dx = 1308,$ and $\int_0^{12} y\,dx = 1140$ by Simpson's Rule; $\int_0^6 y\,dx = -168,$ $\int_6^{12} y\,dx = 1308,$ $\int_0^{12} y\,dx = 1140$ by the three-eighths rule; $\int_0^6 y\,dx = -168,$ $\int_6^{12} y\,dx = 1308,$ and $\int_0^{12} y\,dx = 1140$ by Weddle's Rule.

7. $\int_{x_0}^{x_0+4h} y\,dx = \dfrac{2h}{45}(7y_0 + 32y_1 + 12y_2 + 32y_3 + 7y_4).$

Chapter 4

SECTION 2   Page 64

1. **(a)** $P^2(x) + 3P^1(x) - 4P^0(x)$;

    (b) $2P^3(x) + 7P^2(x) - 4P^1(x) - 4P^0(x)$;

    (c) $P^3(x) + 3P^2(x) + 12P^0(x)$;

    (d) $P^5(x) + 10P^4(x) + 22P^3(x) + 6P^2(x) - P^1(x)$;

    (e) $P^4(x) + 6P^3(x) + 7P^2(x) + P^1(x)$.

2. **(a)** $\dfrac{n}{2}(n + 1)$;

    (b) $\frac{1}{3}(n^3 + 18n^2 - 10n)$;

    (c) $\frac{1}{12}(3n^4 + 10n^3 + 9n^2 + 2n)$;

    (d) $14{,}370$;

    (e) $\frac{1}{3}(n^3 - 3n^2 + 5n)$;

    (f) $\frac{1}{3}(n^3 - 12n^2 + 50n - 69)$ for $n \geq 4$.

3. **(a)** $\frac{1}{4}(n + 1)(n)(n - 1)(n - 2)$;

    (b) $\frac{1}{4}(n^4 + 2n^3 + 7n^2 + 6n)$;

    (c) $\frac{1}{30}(6n^5 + 15n^4 + 10n^3 - n)$;

    (d) $\frac{1}{4}(n + 3)(n + 4)(n + 5)(n + 6) - 90$.

5. $n(n - 1) \cdots (n - k + 1)P^{n-k}(x)$.

6. $\dbinom{x}{n - k}$.

8. $c + \dbinom{x}{1}y_0 + \dbinom{x}{2}\Delta y_0 + \dbinom{x}{3}\Delta^2 y_{-1} + \dbinom{x + 1}{4}\Delta^3 y_{-1}$

    $+ \dbinom{x + 1}{5}\Delta^4 y_{-2} + \dbinom{x + 2}{6}\Delta^5 y_{-2} + \dbinom{x + 2}{7}\Delta^6 y_{-3} + \cdots$.

11. **(a)** $\dfrac{1}{n + 1}P^{n+1}(x) + c$;

    (b) $\dbinom{x}{n + 1} + c$;

    (c) $\frac{1}{4}P^4(x) + \frac{5}{3}P^3(x) - 2P^2(x) + 4P^1(x) + cP^0(x)$.

SECTION 3   Page 68

1. $\dfrac{n(n+3)}{4(n+1)(n+2)}$.

2. $\dfrac{n}{2n+1}$.

3. $\frac{3}{2}n^2 + \frac{3}{2}n + 2(2^n - 1)$.

4. $2^{17} - 1484$.

5. $\dfrac{(b-1)(b-2)(b-3) - (a-1)(a-2)(a-3)}{3(b-1)(b-2)(b-3)(a-1)(a-2)(a-3)}$.

6. $\dfrac{n}{3(3-2n)}$.

7. $\dfrac{e^x + c}{e - 1}$.

SECTION 4   Page 70

1. $\dfrac{3^{n+1}}{4}(2n^2 - 4n + 3) - \frac{9}{4}$.

2. $\dfrac{5}{4} - \dfrac{2n+5}{2(n+1)(n+2)}$.

3. $\dfrac{2n}{n+1}$.

4. $\dfrac{3^n(n+1) - 1}{3^n(n+1)}$.

5. $2^x(x^2 - 4x + 6) + c$.

6. $(n+1)! - 1$.

7. $\dfrac{13}{180}$.

8. $\dfrac{2^{n+1}}{n+2} - 1$.

10. $\dfrac{1}{x+n+1}$.

Chapter 5

SECTION 2   Page 75

1. **(a)** 1.71;   **(b)** 1.41, -1.41;   **(c)** 1.15;   **(d)** 0.79;   **(e)** 1.76;

   (f) 0.82, -0.82;   **(g)** 6.80;   **(h)** 1.22, -2.36;   **(i)** 2.55;

   (j) -1.93.

2. $x_{i+1} = \dfrac{1}{2}\left[x_i + \dfrac{N}{x_i} \right].$

SECTION 3   Page 78

1. $\begin{pmatrix} 0 & -1 & -2 \\ 3 & 2 & 1 \\ 8 & 7 & 6 \end{pmatrix}.$

2. Row i; column j; along the main diagonal.

4. $\begin{pmatrix} -1 & -2 & -4 \\ -3 & 1 & -3 \end{pmatrix}.$

7. If, and only if, $AB = BA$.

10. Yes, if the number of rows of the first matrix is equal to the number of columns of the second matrix.

12. $AB = (x^2 + y^2 + z^2)$;

   $BA = \begin{pmatrix} x^2 & xy & xz \\ yx & y^2 & yz \\ zx & zy & z^2 \end{pmatrix}.$

15. $x_1 = (ae + bg)z_1 + (af + bh)z_2$;

   $x_2 = (ce + dg)z_1 + (cf + dh)z_2.$

SECTION 4   Page 83

1. $\begin{pmatrix} 2 & -\frac{5}{4} \\ -3 & 2 \end{pmatrix}$; $\begin{pmatrix} 1 & 2 \\ 0 & 0 \end{pmatrix}$ has no inverse;

$$\begin{pmatrix} \dfrac{d}{ad-bc} & \dfrac{-b}{ad-bc} \\ \dfrac{-c}{ad-bc} & \dfrac{a}{ad-bc} \end{pmatrix}, \text{ provided } ad - bc \neq 0;$$

$$\begin{pmatrix} -\frac{1}{2} & 1 & \frac{1}{2} \\ \frac{3}{2} & -\frac{3}{2} & -\frac{1}{2} \\ \frac{1}{2} & -\frac{1}{2} & -\frac{1}{2} \end{pmatrix}.$$

7. $(A^{-1})^2$.

SECTION 5   Page 86

1. (a) $x = \frac{7}{5}, y = -\frac{1}{5}, z = 0$;

   (b) $w = 4, x = -\frac{3}{2}, y = -1, z = -\frac{1}{2}$;

   (c) $w = 1, x = 1, y = -2, z = -1$;

   (d) $x = 0, y = 0, z = 0$.

3. $x_1 = -1, x_2 = 3, x_3 = 0, x_4 = -1$.

4. (a) $x = 0, y = 3$; intersecting lines.

   (b) $x = 1, y = -2$; intersecting lines.

   (c) $x = -2 - 3c, y = c$, where c is any real number; coincident lines.

   (d) No solution; parallel lines.

   (e) $x = \dfrac{4b^2 + 4ab + a^2}{3b + a}$, $y = \dfrac{8b^2 + 3ab}{9b + 3a}$, provided $a \neq -3b$; intersecting lines. If $a = -3b$, parallel lines.

   (f) $x = \dfrac{3a^2 - b^2}{3}$, $y = \dfrac{2b}{3}$, provided $b \neq 0$; intersecting lines. If $b = 0$, coincident lines.

5. Linearly dependent: $tf(x, y, z) + 2tg(x, y, z) - th(x, y, z) = 0$, for any real number $t \neq 0$.

SECTION 6   Page 93

1.   **(a)** $x_1 = -8$, $x_2 = 0$, $x_3 = \frac{26}{5}$;
     (b) $x_1 = 5$, $x_2 = 1$, $x_3 = 19$, $x_4 = 25$;
     (c) $x_1 = -\frac{5}{9}$, $x_2 = -\frac{44}{9}$, $x_3 = -\frac{38}{9}$;
     (d) $x_1 = 0$, $x_2 = -2$, $x_3 = 1$;
     (e) $x_1 = \frac{17}{3} + t$, $x_2 = -\frac{1}{3} - t$, $x_3 = t$, for any real number t;
     (f) $x_1 = 3t$, $x_2 = t$, $x_3 = -t$, for any real number t;
     (g) No solution;   **(h)** No solution;   **(i)** $x_1 = 0$, $x_2 = 0$, $x_3 = 0$;
     (j) $x_1 = 1$, $x_2 = -1$, $x_3 = 2$, $x_4 = -3$, $x_5 = 4$.

2.   **(a)** 8;   **(b)** any real number.

4. n^2; $\dfrac{n^2 + n}{2}$.

SECTION 8   Page 100

1.   **(a)** $x_1 = -4$, $x_2 = 2$, $x_3 = 5$;
     (b) $x_1 = 6$, $x_2 = 3$, $x_3 = 8$;
     (c) $x_1 = 1$, $x_2 = 5$, $x_3 = 2$, $x_4 = 3$;
     (d) $x_1 = -2$, $x_2 = -1$, $x_3 = 2$;
     (e) $x_1 = 1$, $x_2 = 2$, $x_3 = 3$.

2.   **(a)** $x_1 = 5$, $x_2 = 3$, $x_3 = 2.5$;
     (b) $x_1 = 2$, $x_2 = 5$, $x_3 = -1$, $x_4 = 1$;
     (c) $x_1 = 15.2$, $x_2 = -8.5$, $x_3 = 12.3$;
     (d) $x_1 = 1$, $x_2 = 2$, $x_3 = -1$, $x_4 = 0$.

Chapter 6

SECTION 2   Page 105

1. $\phi(x) = 2x - 2$.
2. $\phi(x) = 3.7 + 6.7x - 2.2x^2$.
3. $\phi(t) = -0.1 + 0.1t + 16.0t^2$.
4. $\phi(x) = 1 + 3x - x^2$.

5. $a = \dfrac{\sum x^2 \sum y - \sum x \sum xy}{(n+1) \sum x^2 - (\sum x)^2}$, $b = \dfrac{(n+1) \sum xy - \sum x \sum y}{(n+1) \sum x^2 - (\sum x)^2}$.

6. (a) $a = \dfrac{\sum y}{n+1}$, $b = \dfrac{\sum xy}{\sum x^2}$;

   (b) $a = \dfrac{(4n+2) \sum y - 6 \sum xy}{n(n-1)}$, $b = \dfrac{12 \sum xy - (6n+6) \sum y}{(n-1)(n)(n+1)}$.

8. $3x - 3y + 4 = 0$.

11. $f(x, y) = -2x + 3y - 2$.

12. $3x - 4y - 4 = 0$.

SECTION 3   Page 111

1. $\phi(x) = \frac{1}{198}(21x^4 - 325x^3 + 1287x^2 + 643x - 3960)$.

3. (a) $P_0(x) = 1$, $P_1(x) = x - 2$, $P_2(x) = 3x^2 - 12x + 10$;

   (b) $P_0(x) = 1$, $P_1(x) = 2x - 5$, $P_2(x) = x^2 - 5x + 5$,

   $P_3(x) = \frac{1}{3}(10x^3 - 75x^2 + 167x - 105)$.

4. $\phi(x) = \frac{9}{2}$ with $\sum R_i^2 = 25$; $\phi(x) = \frac{1}{10}(16x + 5)$ with $\sum R_i^2 = 12.2$;

   $\phi(x) = \frac{1}{10}(15x^2 - 59x + 80)$ with $\sum R_i^2 = 3.2$;

   $\phi(x) = \frac{1}{30}(-40x^3 + 345x^2 - 845x + 660)$ with $\sum R_i^2 = 0$.

SECTION 4   Page 115

1. $y = 0.34x^{2.22}$.

2. $p = 12.33v^{-1.01}$.

3. $y = 2.97e^{1.014x}$.

4. $n = 1.08e^{1.239t}$.

5. Let $z = \dfrac{1}{y}$.

6. $y = \dfrac{1}{1.82 + 0.61x}$.

SECTION 5   Page 119

1. $0.61x - 0.26y + 1 = 0$.

2. (a) $\phi(x) = -0.50 + 0.71x$;

(b) $\phi(y) = 0.93 + 1.30y$;

(c) $1.27x - 1.74y - 1 = 0$.

4.
$$\begin{cases} \sum w_i a_0 + \sum w_i x_i a_1 + \cdots + \sum w_i x_i^k a_k = \sum w_i y_i, \\ \sum w_i x_i a_0 + \sum w_i x_i^2 a_1 + \cdots + \sum w_i x_i^{k+1} a_k = \sum w_i x_i y_i, \\ \cdots \\ \sum w_i x_i^k a_0 + \sum w_i x_i^{k+1} a_1 + \cdots + \sum w_i x_i^{2k} a_k = \sum w_i x_i^k y_i. \end{cases}$$

All the summations are over i from 1 to n.

5. $\phi(x) = \frac{1}{18}(56 - 19x + 50x^2)$.

Chapter 7

SECTION 3   **Page 127**

4. $f(x) = \dfrac{\pi^2}{6} - 2\left[\cos x - \dfrac{\cos 2x}{4} + \dfrac{\cos 3x}{9} - \cdots + \dfrac{(-1)^{n+1}\cos nx}{n^2} + \cdots\right]$

$\qquad + \dfrac{(\pi^2 - 4)\sin x}{\pi} - \dfrac{\pi \sin 2x}{2} + \cdots$

$\qquad + \dfrac{[(2 - n^2\pi^2)(-1)^n - 2]\sin nx}{n^3\pi} + \cdots.$

5. $f(x) = \dfrac{8}{\pi}\left[\cos x + \dfrac{\cos 3x}{9} + \dfrac{\cos 5x}{25} + \cdots + \dfrac{\cos(2n-1)x}{(2n-1)^2} + \cdots\right].$

6. $f(x) = \dfrac{\pi^2}{3k} - \dfrac{4}{k}\left[\cos x - \dfrac{\cos 2x}{2^2} + \dfrac{\cos 3x}{3^2}\right.$

$\qquad \left. - \dfrac{\cos 4x}{4^2} + \cdots + \dfrac{(-1)^{n+1}\cos nx}{n^2} + \cdots\right].$

7. $f(x) = \dfrac{1}{\pi} + \dfrac{\sin x}{2} - \dfrac{2}{\pi}\left[\dfrac{\cos 2x}{3} + \dfrac{\cos 4x}{15}\right.$

$\qquad \left. + \dfrac{\cos 6x}{35} + \cdots + \dfrac{\cos 2nx}{(2n)^2 - 1} + \cdots\right].$

8. $f(x) = \dfrac{e^\pi - e^{-\pi}}{\pi}\left[\dfrac{1}{2} - \dfrac{\cos x}{2} + \dfrac{\cos 2x}{5} - \dfrac{\cos 3x}{10} + \cdots\right.$

$\qquad + \dfrac{(-1)^n \cos nx}{n^2 + 1} + \cdots + \dfrac{\sin x}{2} - \dfrac{2 \sin 2x}{5}$

$\qquad \left. + \dfrac{3 \sin 3x}{10} - \cdots + \dfrac{(-1)^{n+1}n \sin nx}{n^2 + 1} + \cdots\right].$

9. $f(x) = 2[\cos x + \cos 3x + \cdots + \cos (2n - 1)x + \cdots].$

10. $f(x) = \dfrac{2}{\pi} + \dfrac{4}{\pi}\left[\dfrac{\cos 2x}{3} - \dfrac{\cos 4x}{15} + \dfrac{\cos 6x}{35} - \cdots\right.$

$\qquad \left. + \dfrac{(-1)^{n+1} \cos nx}{4n^2 - 1} + \cdots\right].$

SECTION 5   Page 132

1. **(a)** Even;   **(b)** odd;   **(c)** even;   **(d)** even;   **(e)** odd;
(f) neither odd nor even;   **(g)** odd;   **(h)** even;   **(i)** even;
(j) even.

2. **(a)** 0;   **(b)** 0.

4. $f(x) = \displaystyle\sum_{n=1}^{\infty} \dfrac{h}{n} \cdot \sin\dfrac{n\alpha\pi}{2} [1 - (-1)^n] \cos nx.$

5. $f(x) = 2h\left[\cos x - \dfrac{\cos 3x}{3} + \dfrac{\cos 5x}{5} - \dfrac{\cos 7x}{7} + \cdots\right.$

$\qquad \left. + \dfrac{(-1)^{n+1} \cos (2n - 1)x}{2n - 1} + \cdots\right].$

6. $f(x) = \dfrac{4}{\pi}\left[\cos x + \dfrac{\cos 3x}{9} + \dfrac{\cos 5x}{25} + \cdots + \dfrac{\cos (2n - 1)x}{(2n - 1)^2} + \cdots\right].$

7. $f(x) = \dfrac{4}{\pi}\left[\dfrac{1}{2} - \dfrac{\cos 2x}{1\cdot 3} - \dfrac{\cos 4x}{3\cdot 5} - \dfrac{\cos 6x}{5\cdot 7} - \cdots\right.$

$\qquad \left. - \dfrac{\cos 2nx}{(2n - 1)(2n + 1)} - \cdots\right].$

8. $f(x) = \dfrac{\pi}{2} + 2\left[\sin x + \dfrac{\sin 3x}{3} + \dfrac{\sin 5x}{5} + \cdots + \dfrac{\sin (2n - 1)x}{2n - 1} + \cdots\right].$

9. $f(x) = \dfrac{2k \sin k\pi}{\pi}\left[\dfrac{1}{2k^2} - \left(\dfrac{\cos x}{k^2 - 1^2} - \dfrac{\cos 2x}{k^2 - 2^2} + \dfrac{\cos 3x}{k^2 - 3^2} - \cdots\right.\right.$

$\qquad \left.\left. + \dfrac{(-1)^{n+1} \cos nx}{k^2 - n^2} + \cdots\right)\right].$

SECTION 6   Page 136

1. $\dfrac{2}{\pi}\left[\cos 2x + \dfrac{\cos 6x}{9} + \dfrac{\cos 10x}{25} + \cdots + \dfrac{\cos 2(2n-1)x}{(2n-1)^2} + \cdots\right].$

2. $\dfrac{4A}{\pi}\left[\sin 2x + \dfrac{\sin 6x}{3} + \dfrac{\sin 10x}{5} + \cdots + \dfrac{\sin 2(2n-1)x}{2n-1} + \cdots\right].$

3. $\dfrac{4}{\pi}\left[\sin \pi x + \dfrac{\sin 3\pi x}{3} + \dfrac{\sin 5\pi x}{5} + \cdots + \dfrac{\sin (2n-1)\pi x}{2n-1} + \cdots\right].$

4. $f(x) = \dfrac{1}{4} - \dfrac{2}{\pi^2}\left[\cos \pi x + \dfrac{\cos 3\pi x}{9} + \dfrac{\cos 5\pi x}{25} + \cdots\right.$

$\qquad\left. + \dfrac{\cos (2n-1)\pi x}{(2n-1)^2} + \cdots\right]$

$\qquad + \dfrac{1}{\pi}\left[\sin \pi x - \dfrac{\sin 2\pi x}{2} + \dfrac{\sin 3\pi x}{3} - \cdots\right.$

$\qquad\left. + \dfrac{(-1)^{n+1}\sin n\pi x}{n} + \cdots\right].$

5. $-\dfrac{1}{3} + \dfrac{4}{\pi^2}\left[\cos \pi x - \dfrac{\cos 2\pi x}{4} + \dfrac{\cos 3\pi x}{9} - \cdots + \dfrac{(-1)^{n+1}\cos n\pi x}{n^2} + \cdots\right]$

$\qquad + \dfrac{2}{\pi}\left[\sin \pi x - \dfrac{\sin 2\pi x}{2} + \dfrac{\sin 3\pi x}{3} - \cdots + \dfrac{(-1)^{n+1}\sin n\pi x}{n} + \cdots\right].$

6. $2\pi^3 + 12\pi\left[\cos x + \dfrac{\cos 2x}{2} + \dfrac{\cos 3x}{3} + \cdots + \dfrac{\cos nx}{n} + \cdots\right.$

$\qquad + 4\left[\left(\dfrac{3}{1^3} - \dfrac{2\pi^2}{1}\right)\sin x + \left(\dfrac{3}{2^3} - \dfrac{2\pi^2}{2}\right)\sin 2x + \left(\dfrac{3}{3^3} - \dfrac{2\pi^2}{3}\right)\sin 3x\right.$

$\qquad\left. + \cdots + \left(\dfrac{3}{n^3} - \dfrac{2\pi^2}{n}\right)\sin nx + \cdots\right].$

8. (a) $1 + 2k\left[\sin x - \dfrac{\sin 2x}{2} + \dfrac{\sin 3x}{3} - \cdots + \dfrac{(-1)^{n+1}\sin nx}{n} + \cdots\right];$

(b) $1 + k\pi - 2k\left[\sin x + \dfrac{\sin 2x}{2} + \dfrac{\sin 3x}{3} + \cdots + \dfrac{\sin nx}{n} + \cdots\right];$

(c) $1 + \dfrac{k\pi}{2} - \dfrac{4k}{\pi}\left[\cos x + \dfrac{\cos 3x}{9} + \dfrac{\cos 5x}{25} + \cdots\right.$

$\qquad\left. + \dfrac{\cos (2n-1)x}{(2n-1)^2} + \cdots\right];$

(d) $\dfrac{2}{\pi}\left[(k\pi + 2)\sin x - \dfrac{(k\pi)\sin 2x}{2} + \dfrac{(k\pi + 2)\sin 3x}{3} - \cdots\right.$

$\qquad\left. + \dfrac{[(k\pi + 1)(-1)^{n+1} + 1]\sin nx}{n} + \cdots\right].$

SECTION 7   Page 141

1. $T(x) = 2.750000 + 1.699358 \cos x - 0.666667 \cos 2x$
$+ 0.333333 \cos 3x - 0.032692 \cos 5x - 0.083333 \cos 6x$
$- 0.788675 \sin x + 0.500000 \sin 3x - 0.211325 \sin 5x.$

2. $T(x) = \frac{1}{3}[6 - \cos x - 6 \cos 2x + 2 \cos 3x - \cos 5x].$

3. $T(x) = \frac{1}{6}\left[62 - 41 \cos \frac{\pi x}{3} + 19 \cos \frac{2\pi x}{3} + 20 \cos \pi x \right.$
$\left. + 126.43965 \sin \frac{\pi x}{3} - 15.58845 \sin \frac{2\pi x}{3} \right].$

Chapter 8

SECTION 2   Page 146

9. 1.25.

10. 0.5.

11. 0.5.

12. −1.

SECTION 4   Page 153

1. 0.3; exact, 0.3.

2. 0; exact, 0.149.

3. 2; exact, 1.785.

4. 2.3; exact, 2.327.

5.

x	0	0.1	0.2	0.3	0.4
y	1	1.1	1.231	1.403	1.630

6.

x	0	0.1	0.2	0.3	0.4	0.5
y (approx.)	1	1.3	1.655	2.069	2.546	3.092
y (exact)	1	1.331	1.728	2.197	2.744	3.375

7. $y = 1.125.$

8.

x	0	0.5	1.0
y	1	2	3
z	2	2.5	3.75

9. 0.167.

10. 1.750.

11. 2.327.

12.

x	0	0.1	0.2	0.3	0.4	0.5
y	1	1.332	1.730	2.200	2.748	3.380

SECTION 5   Page 157

1. $y = 1 - x + x^2 - \dfrac{2x^3}{3} + \dfrac{5x^4}{6} - \dfrac{4x^5}{5} + \cdots.$

2. $y = 1 + \dfrac{x^2}{2} + \dfrac{1}{2!}\left(\dfrac{x^2}{2}\right)^2 + \dfrac{1}{3!}\left(\dfrac{x^2}{2}\right)^3 + \dfrac{1}{4!}\left(\dfrac{x^2}{2}\right)^4 + \dfrac{1}{5!}\left(\dfrac{x^2}{2}\right)^5 + \cdots;$

$y = e^{x^2/2}.$

3. $y = \dfrac{\pi}{2} + \left(\dfrac{\pi}{2}\right)x + \left(\dfrac{\pi}{2} + 1\right)\dfrac{x^2}{2!} + \left(\dfrac{\pi}{2} + 1\right)\dfrac{x^3}{3!} + \left(\dfrac{\pi}{2}\right)\dfrac{x^4}{4!} + \left(\dfrac{\pi}{2}\right)\dfrac{x^5}{5!} + \cdots;$

$y = \left(\dfrac{\pi + 1}{2}\right)e^x - \tfrac{1}{2}(\sin x + \cos x).$

4. $y = 2 + 2x + x^2 + \dfrac{x^3}{3!} + \dfrac{x^4}{4!} + \cdots; y = 1 + x + \dfrac{x^2}{2} + e^x.$

5. 1.106.

6. 0.203.

7. 1.201.

8. 0.221.

10. $y = 1 - x + \dfrac{2x^2}{2!} + \dfrac{2x^4}{4!} + \dfrac{2x^6}{6!} + \cdots,$

$z = -1 + x + \dfrac{2x^3}{3!} + \dfrac{2x^5}{5!} + \dfrac{2x^7}{7!} + \cdots;$

$y = e^x + e^{-x} - x - 1, \; z = e^x - e^{-x} - x - 1.$

SECTION 6   Page 161

1. $y_4(x) = 1 - x + x^2 - \dfrac{x^3}{3} + \dfrac{x^4}{12} - \dfrac{x^5}{120}.$

2. $y_4(x) = x + x^2 + \dfrac{x^3}{3} + \dfrac{x^4}{12} + \dfrac{x^5}{120}.$

3. $y_4(x) = 1 + x + \dfrac{x^2}{2} + \dfrac{x^3}{3} + \dfrac{x^4}{8} + \dfrac{x^5}{15} + \dfrac{x^6}{48} + \dfrac{x^7}{105} + \dfrac{x^8}{384}.$

4. $y_4(x) = 1 + 2x - \dfrac{x^2}{2} - \dfrac{x^3}{2} - \dfrac{x^4}{4} + \dfrac{x^5}{12} - \dfrac{11x^6}{360} + \dfrac{x^7}{252} - \dfrac{x^8}{2016}.$

5. 1.470.

6. 1.526.

SECTION 7   Page 166

1.

x	y (modified Euler)	y (exact)	y (Runge-Kutta)
0.4	1.467	1.470	1.470

2. 0.243.

3. 1.127.

4. 5.362.

5.

x	y (exact)	y (Euler)	y (Runge-Kutta)
0	2.000	2.000	2.000
0.1	2.205	2.200	2.205
0.2	2.421	2.410	2.421
0.3	2.650	2.631	2.650
0.4	2.892	2.864	2.892
0.5	3.149	3.110	3.149
0.6	3.422	3.371	3.422
0.7	3.714	3.648	3.714
0.8	4.026	3.943	4.026
0.9	4.360	4.257	4.360
1.0	4.718	4.593	4.719

6. 0.254.

INDEX

1234567890